Nonfiction Reading Comprehension
5-6

Written by
Sarah McFadden Fornara

Editors: Carla Hamaguchi and Collene Dobelmann
Illustrator: Dimension
Designer/Production: Moonhee Pak/Carrie Rickmond
Cover Designer: Barbara Peterson
Art Director: Tom Cochrane
Project Director: Carolea Williams

Table of Contents

Introduction

Each book in the *Power Practice*™ series contains dozens of ready-to-use activity pages to provide students with skill practice. Use the fun activities to supplement and enhance what you are already teaching in your classroom. Give an activity page to students as independent class work, or send the pages home as homework to reinforce skills taught in class. An answer key is provided for quick reference.

Nonfiction Reading Comprehension 5–6 is filled with grade-level nonfiction reading selections and follow-up activities. The activities include the following skills:
- summarizing and paraphrasing
- making inferences
- determining cause and effect
- sequencing
- recognizing relevant and irrelevant details
- restating
- classifiying
- forming judgements
- recognizing main ideas and details
- using context clues
- using graphic organizers
- accessing prior knowledge
- making personal connections
- questioning

The activities provide entertaining and informative texts that are grounded in the curriculum taught in the fifth and sixth grades. They give information to activate schema for a variety of content area lessons that a student may encounter in his or her textbooks. The reading selections also aim to appeal to fifth and sixth graders' interest in odd facts and lurid details.

Higher-level thinking skills are stressed throughout the book with at least one activity per text selection. There are also a number of activities that are appropriate for or can be easily adapted for struggling readers. There is a focus on writing activities with opportunities to write formal and informal letters, paragraphs, comparison and persuasive essays, and newspaper articles. These provide ample ways for students to demonstrate mastery of standards in writing.

Use these ready-to-go activities to "recharge" skill review and give students the power to succeed!

Black Holes

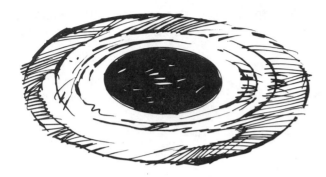

They come in all sizes, from the size of an atom to a weight equivalent to a billion of our suns. Many came into being 15 billion years ago when our universe was created. Others are created whenever a star explodes in a supernova. Scientists know they exist even though they have never seen one. Scientists had theories about them for many years before Archibald Wheeler gave them the name "black hole" in 1967.

A black hole begins its life as a star, but not just any star. Our own sun will never have what it takes to be a black hole. It takes a star at least ten times heavier and more often hundreds of times bigger than our sun to create a black hole. These stars are called red supergiants. They burn their fuel more quickly than other kinds of stars. This creates intense heat and pressure, which cause an iron core to develop. The iron core cannot be compressed further, so no energy can be gained from its fusion. Eventually, the imbalance of energy causes the star to explode in a supernova.

After the supernova, one of two things happens in just a few seconds. Both are the result of the collapse of the supernova's core. One result could be the creation of a neutron star, called a pulsar. Like the revolving light on a police car, these neutron stars give off bursts of radiation from their two poles as they rotate in space. The second result occurs if the supernova is too heavy to become a pulsar. The gravity is so great that it keeps collapsing and collapsing until it becomes a black hole.

Gravity is the key to a black hole. It is what creates one and it is what lets us know a black hole exists. The gravity of a black hole has strange effects on the other light in space. If a black hole is between Earth and another galaxy, that galaxy will seem to be split into two pieces. It also appears brighter and fools us into thinking the galaxy is closer than it is. We cannot see a black hole itself, but its gravity captures light, which forms a faint ring—an accretion disk—around the hole, giving a clue that it is there.

Light is not the only kind of radiation affected by black holes, however. The first black hole was detected around 1970, because the satellite *Uhuru* was able to measure x-ray signals that were caused by gas being sucked from a supergiant star into the nearby black hole. More recent observations in February of 2004 show that black holes rip apart stars that get too close, devouring some parts and allowing the rest of the matter to escape into the universe. Scientists believe this is the way black holes grow.

Some scientists had theories that it might be possible to travel through black holes to other universes or even to travel through time. Recent developments in the science of black holes have changed these theories, and this kind of travel no longer seems possible.

Stephen Hawking is probably the most well-known scientist who studies black holes. In July of 2004, he reevaluated an idea about black holes that he had held since the 1970s. Originally, Hawking thought that everything that fell into a black hole was destroyed or shot out into another universe. Other scientists disagreed, however, because this destruction of matter doesn't agree with Einstein's famous equation $E=mc^2$, which basically means that nothing is ever really destroyed. Hawking now says, "If you jump into a black hole, your mass energy will be returned to our universe, but in a mangled form which contains the information about what you were like, but in an unrecognizable state." At least, that is the theory for now. Maybe you will come up with something new in the future.

Nonfiction Reading Comprehension • 5–6 © 2005 Creative Teaching Press

Name _____ Date _____

Out of This World

Use words from the passage to fill in the blanks. Then write the correct letter for each number to reveal the answer to the riddle.

1 a group of stars, planets, and other matter ___ ___ ___ ___ ___ ___
1   2   3   4   5   6

2 waves of energy ___ ___ ___ ___ ___ ___ ___ ___ ___
7   8   9   10 11 12 13 14 15

3 the center c o r e
16 17 18 19

4 another name for the Milky Way galaxy ___ ___ ___ ___ ___ ___ ___ ___
20 21 22 23 24 25 26 27

5 opposite ends of the axis ___ ___ ___ ___ ___
28 29 30 31 32

6 the explosion of a large star ___ ___ ___ ___ ___ ___ ___ ___ ___
33 34 35 36 37 38 39 40 41

7 short wavelength radiation ___ - ___ ___ ___
42   43 44 45

8 a young neutron star that gives off radiation ___ ___ ___ ___ ___ ___
46 47 48 49 50 51

9 the smallest portion of an element ___ ___ ___ ___
52 53 54 55

10 a very massive star ___ ___ ___ ___ ___ ___ ___ ___ ___ ___
56 57 58 59 60 61 62 63 64 65

11 one kind of atom turns into another and releases energy ___ ___ ___ ___ ___ ___
66 67 68 69 70 71

12 a collapsed star ___ ___ ___ ___ ___ ___ ___   ___ ___ ___ ___
72 73 74 75 76 77 78   79 80 81 82

13 an idea based on science ___ ___ ___ ___ ___ ___
83 84 85 86 87 88

14 pushing force ___ ___ ___ ___ ___ ___ ___ ___
89 90 91 92 93 94 95 96

15 glow around hole ___ ___ ___ ___ ___ ___ ___ ___ ___   ___ ___ ___ ___
97 98 99 100 101 102 103 104 105   106 107 108 109

What songs do planets like to sing? ___ ___ ___ ___ ___ ___ ___ ___
21 36 46 65 74 78 101 108

Nonfiction Reading Comprehension • 5–6 © 2005 Creative Teaching Press

Name _____ Date _____

Name That Star

Match each star with its description. You may want to use a reference book for help or read each description carefully for clues.
Here are some hints:

- A star the size of our sun or smaller is a dwarf.
- A star ten to one hundred times the size of the sun is a giant.
- Cool stars are red.
- Hot stars are blue.

1 _____ red giant

2 _B_ red supergiant

3 _____ blue giant

4 _____ blue supergiant

5 _____ white dwarf

6 _____ brown dwarf

7 _____ red dwarf

8 _I_ neutron star

9 _____ protostar

a. a collapsed cloud of gas and dust that did not have enough mass to start nuclear fusion in its core; it is more dense than a planet and produces its own dim light

b. the type of star that may create a black hole after it explodes into a supernova

c. a star bigger than Earth that has a low temperature

d. a bright star that is bigger than Earth and has a high temperature

e. a star near the end of its life that has run out of nuclear fuel; it has collapsed and is very small and light-colored

f. small stars that only give off faint light and are cool

g. clouds of glowing gas and dust that will eventually come together to become stars

h. the brightest, hottest, largest star

i. the result of a supernova; a star that is made up mostly of neutrons

How Does It Happen?

Cut out the steps in the creation of a black hole. Glue them in order below.

<table>
<tr><td></td></tr>
<tr><td></td></tr>
<tr><td></td></tr>
<tr><td></td></tr>
<tr><td></td></tr>
<tr><td></td></tr>
<tr><td></td></tr>
</table>

A black hole is formed.
The star explodes in a supernova.
A massive star begins to run out of fuel.
Gravity is so strong that the object keeps collapsing.
The star begins to develop a core of iron.
The leftovers of the star begin collapsing.
The iron cannot be compressed anymore.

Nonfiction Reading Comprehension • 5–6 © 2005 Creative Teaching Press

A Black Hole

Tell what is happening in each picture as a black hole is created. Write your explanations.

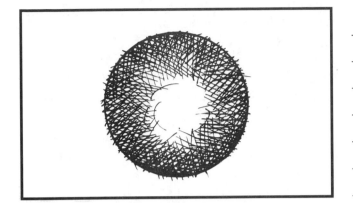

_____
_____
_____
_____
_____
_____
_____

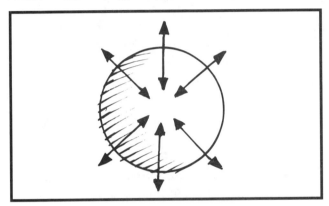

_____
_____
_____
_____
_____
_____
_____
_____

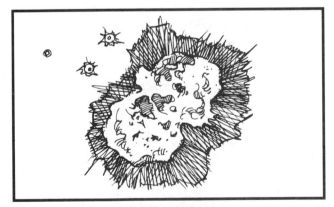

_____
_____
_____
_____
_____
_____
_____
_____

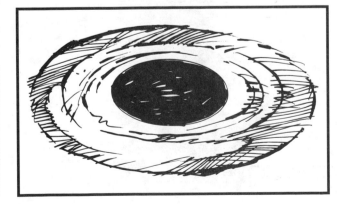

_____
_____
_____
_____
_____
_____
_____

Space Pioneers

What would it be like to float high above Earth in space? "I marveled at the beauty of our planet. People of the world! Let us safeguard and enhance this beauty—not destroy it!" is what Yuri Gagarin (YUR-ee Ga-GAR-in) said. He was the first person to go beyond Earth's atmosphere. Other Earthlings, however, made it into space before he did.

Almost four years before Yuri Gagarin's flight, a dog named Laika became the first living thing in space. Laika flew aboard *Sputnik 2* in November of 1957. She was the first of thirteen dogs to be part of the Soviet Union's space program. A dog name Zvezdochka, which means "Little Star," went into space on March 25, 1961. Her flight was a chance to see how things would work for the *Vostok 1* flight, which would take the first human into space.

On April 12, 1961, twenty-seven-year-old cosmonaut Yuri Gagarin lifted off from Baiknour, Kazachstan, then part of the Soviet Union. His space flight was only 108 minutes long, but that was a significant accomplishment for space exploration at the time.

Dogs were not the only animals to help prepare for human space flight. Several early flights had rats, mice, and guinea pigs on board. France even launched two cats. The main animals used in the American space program were monkeys. Five were launched between December 13, 1958, and January 21, 1960.

Two chimpanzees, Ham and Enos, also made the trip beyond Earth's boundaries. Ham's flight on January 31, 1961, made it possible for the first American to journey into space.

Freedom 7 launched from Cape Canaveral on May 5, 1961. Astronaut Alan Shepard was on board for a fifteen minute and twenty-two second flight. The difference between Gagarin's flight in April and Shepard's in May is that Shepard was able to control his spacecraft, and Gagarin could not.

Three months later, on August 6, 1961, the Soviet Union launched *Vostok 2*. Cosmonaut Gherman Titov stayed in orbit for twenty-five hours and eighteen minutes. Titov was able to orbit Earth seventeen and a half times.

The first American to orbit Earth was John Glenn. He orbited Earth three times on February 20, 1962, in the spacecraft *Friendship 7*. His flight lasted four hours, fifty-five minutes, and twenty-three seconds. As he watched the Earth speed by below him and the sun set, Glenn said, "That was about the shortest day I've ever run into."

The first woman in space was Valentina Tereshkova. She was launched into space in *Vostok 6* on June 16, 1963. She spent nearly three days making forty-eight orbits of our planet.

There have been many advances in space exploration in the past forty years. Men have walked on the moon, the International Space Station is being constructed, and the space shuttles make regular flights. With the launch of *Spaceship 1* on June 21, 2004, there is now the possibility that anyone who can pay the high cost will be able to travel into space like these pioneers. Perhaps someday you will be the one describing what Earth looks like from space.

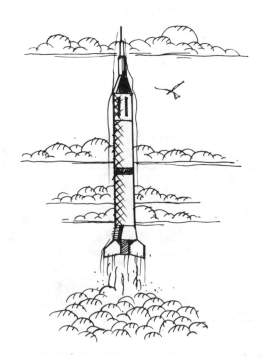

Nonfiction Reading Comprehension • 5–6 © 2005 Creative Teaching Press

Name _____ Date _____

Astronaut or Cosmonaut?

The Russians called their explorers cosmonauts and the Americans called theirs astronauts. Why did they call them by different names?

The Russians used the prefix "cosmo," which comes from the Greek word *kosmos*, meaning "universe." The Americans used the prefix "astro," which comes from the Latin prefix *astro-*, meaning "star." These prefixes do not have the exact same meaning, but they are similar. You would find other words with these prefixes when studying more about space.

Fill in the chart with prefixes you might find when reading about certain subjects. How many do you know already? Use a dictionary to find the meanings of the rest.

acous-	cyto-	hexa-	phyto-
aero-	deca-	ichthyo-	rhizo-
andro-	dodeca-	luni-	septi-
anthropo-	ethno-	oculo-	stelli-
atmo-	gluc-	oro-	uni-
avi-	helio-	oto-	
centi-	hepta-	pedo-	

1 Prefixes you might find in words when you are studying about space	astro- cosmo-
2 Prefixes you might find in words when you are studying about the five senses	
3 Prefixes you might find in words when you are studying about living things	
4 Prefixes you might find in words when you are studying about people	
5 Prefixes you might find in words when you are studying about numbers	

Dogs or Monkeys?

The United States used monkeys and chimpanzees as space pioneers. The Soviet space program used dogs. Why do you think they chose different animals? Do you think it was better to use dogs or monkeys? Fill in the charts with pros and cons for using each animal. Then complete the paragraph.

Dogs

Good things about using them	Bad things about using them

Monkeys and Chimpanzees

Good things about using them	Bad things about using them

If I were running a space program, I would use _____ instead of _____.
They are _____

_____

_____

unlike _____, which are _____

_____.

The worst thing about using _____ is _____

_____.

Nonfiction Reading Comprehension • 5–6 © 2005 Creative Teaching Press

Name _____ Date _____

Visual Aids

Look at the passage "Space Pioneers." Skim the passage for the information to complete the timeline and graph. Write the events that happened to complete the timeline. Write the name of the astronaut or cosmonaut who completed the space flights to complete the graph.

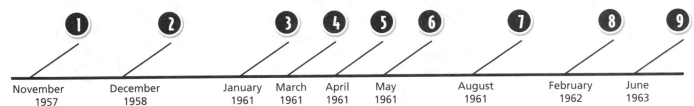

① November 1957   **②** December 1958   **③** January 1961   **④** March 1961   **⑤** April 1961   **⑥** May 1961   **⑦** August 1961   **⑧** February 1962   **⑨** June 1963

① _____

② _____

③ _____

④ _____

⑤ _____

⑥ _____

⑦ _____

⑧ _____

⑨ _____

Time in Space

⑩ _____

Astronaut or Cosmonaut

⑪ _____

⑫ _____

⑬ _____

⑭ _____

15 min., 22 sec.   1 hr., 48 min.   4 hr., 55 min., 23 sec.   25 hr., 18 min.   3 days

Nonfiction Reading Comprehension • 5–6 © 2005 Creative Teaching Press

Creatures of the Day and Night

Animals' bodies adjust to their environment and to their needs for food, shelter, and safety. Some animals adapt so that there is less competition for these things. One of these adaptations is in their sleep patterns. Certain animals are awake during the day, hunting for food while others find shelter and sleep. At the end of the day, the sleepers awaken and go out to hunt, and those who have been active during daylight hours seek a safe place to rest.

Animals who are active during the day are called diurnal. The largest diurnal animals are humans. In many mammals, including humans, metabolism and body temperature drop at night. Some diurnal animals are negatively affected by darkness. They do not function well and may have more difficulty learning when it is dark than when it is light. We are probably most familiar with the diurnal animals since they are the ones that are awake when we are. We put many of these animals, such as horses, donkeys, camels, and llamas, to work for us. Though they may take a lot of naps, animals such as pigs and dogs are still considered diurnal.

Animals that are active during the night are called nocturnal. We all can think of several kinds of animals that are well known for coming out at nighttime, such as owls, wolves, and bats. In the United States, animals such as the armadillo, opossum, porcupine, and raccoon can be seen if you are out at night. Some nocturnal animals in other countries are koalas, rhinoceroses, and tigers. Many rain forest creatures are nocturnal as well.

Being active at night requires additional adaptations. Some animals develop a very good sense of hearing to protect themselves from predators in the dark. Others have the ability to see better in the dark. The pigments around the eyes of some insects will even migrate to increase their light sensitivity. Fireflies light up and crickets chirp to help them attract mates in the dark.

There are some animals that are not really

diurnal or nocturnal. These animals are called crepuscular, and they are most active at dawn and at dusk—the twilight hours when it is not really light but not really dark either. Many desert animals have adapted to a crepuscular life to conserve energy and water in the hot climate. Some rain forest dwellers also deal with the heat in this way. Deer and rabbits are crepuscular. It makes sense then that their main predators, wild cats—such as pumas—would be crepuscular, too. Probably everyone's least favorite crepuscular animal is the mosquito!

You may have seen animals in the wild or in a zoo that are active at times which are not natural for them. For example, you may have seen a fox, which is normally nocturnal, out during the day. Unfortunately, humans have a way of disrupting the natural sleep cycles of some animals. What kind of an effect could that have? The animals must adapt, or they will not survive. Also, some animals adjust the times they are awake according to the season or even the phase of the moon. Some do it to make sure they have the most hunting time possible. Others keep cool in the summer by being nocturnal and keep warm in the winter by being diurnal. Finally, some adapt to provide the greatest amount of safety for their young.

Sleep is very important to animals. Some species spend as much as twenty-two hours a day snoozing. Whether they have decided to get this rest during the day or at night, it is because in order to survive they must be sure to find adequate food and shelter. They must be able to protect themselves and their babies. The next time you see an animal, think about how being diurnal, nocturnal, or crepuscular helps it meet these goals.

Nonfiction Reading Comprehension • 5–6 © 2005 Creative Teaching Press

Name _____ Date _____

Animal Babies

calf	chick	cockerel	eyas	cria	cub	cygnet
ephyna	fawn	fingerling	foal	fry	gosling	~~tadpole~~
hatchling	joey	kid	kit	kitten	leveret	pinkie
poult	puggle	pullet	pup	squab	whelp	

Write the name of each animal's baby in the puzzle.

Across

6. ~~turkey~~
7. ~~whale~~
9. ~~cat~~
10. ~~hawk~~
12. ~~goose~~
14. ~~swan~~
18. ~~platypus~~
19. ~~raccoon~~
20. ~~penguin~~
21. ~~seal~~
22. ~~fish~~
23. ~~hare~~
24. ~~otter~~

Down

1. ~~pigeon~~
2. ~~alligator~~
3. ~~jellyfish~~
4. ~~fox~~
5. ~~salmon~~
8. ~~deer~~
9. ~~goat~~
11. ~~kangaroo~~
13. ~~horse~~
14. ~~rooster~~
15. ~~frog~~
16. ~~mouse~~
17. ~~chicken~~
20. ~~llama~~

Name _____ Date _____

Why Do They Do That?

Circle the causes in column one that could lead to the effects in column two.

Causes	Effect
1. They eat other birds. They nest on cliff ledges. Females are larger than the males. It is the fastest flying bird.	Peregrine falcons are diurnal.
2. They live in desert climates. They eat rodents. They have good eyesight and hearing. They mate for life.	Coyotes are nocturnal.
3. They do not have any natural defenses. Their pouches face backwards to keep dirt out. They eat insects, mice, worms, fruit, and seeds. They have large ears and eyes.	Bandicoots are crepuscular.

Circle the effects in column two that could be due to the causes in column one.

Causes	Effect
Prairie dogs are diurnal.	4. They live in groups for protection. Their main predator is the black- footed ferret. They have large eyes. They live in burrows.
Leopards are nocturnal.	5. Some have black fur. They have good eyesight. They are a threatened species. Males are larger than females.
Red pandas are crepuscular.	6. They weigh about twelve pounds. They like to eat bamboo, fruit, insects, and eggs. They spend most of their time in trees. They have long tails.

Nonfiction Reading Comprehension • 5–6 © 2005 Creative Teaching Press

Name _____ Date _____

Say It Again

Complete the paragraph about each type of animal by writing details for each main idea.

Diurnal animals are most active during the day. _____

_____

_____

_____

_____

_____

_____

_____

At dawn and at dusk, you will see crepuscular animals. _____

_____

_____

_____

_____

_____

_____

_____

_____

_____

_____

Nighttime is when nocturnal animals are active. _____

_____

_____

_____

_____

_____

_____

_____

_____

_____

Active Animals

Read the description of each animal and decide if it is diurnal, nocturnal, or crepuscular. Write **diurnal**, **nocturnal**, or **crepuscular** on the line.

1 This animal spends most of its time in the trees of the rain forests of Madagascar. It builds a nest of leaves and twigs in the fork of a tree and sleeps there during the day. It is an endangered species. This creature is a primate with a long, bushy tail, big eyes and ears, and fur that is black. It has long middle fingers on its hands for digging larvae out of tree bark. It also eats insects and fruit.

_____

2 This endangered animal lives in small family groups in the coastal rain forests of Brazil. It is about the size of a squirrel but has golden fur and a mane like a lion. It is a primate with a long tail. It eats plants and small animals. It spends most of its time in the trees, trying to avoid predators like eagles and hawks. While it sleeps at night, it is in danger from jaguars and ocelots.

_____

3 This animal lives alone in the grasslands and rain forests of New Zealand. It is the only flightless parrot. It is endangered now because of predators settlers brought with them to New Zealand. This creature's name means "night parrot" in the language of the native Maori. It has an owl-like face and soft, green feathers. It can weigh over 8 pounds.

_____

4 This animal is the only venomous lizard in North America. It lives in the deserts of the United States and Mexico. It can survive for months without food, relying on the fat it stores in its tail. This creature eats mice, rats, lizards, birds, and frogs. It will also eat eggs. It avoids the heat of the day, trying to conserve the water in its scaly, pink, yellow, and black-skinned body.

_____

Nonfiction Reading Comprehension • 5–6 © 2005 Creative Teaching Press

Horns, Antlers, and Tusks

Have you ever seen a four-legged animal with two things growing out of its head? What are those things? Are they horns? Are they antlers? Are they tusks? Depending on the animal you are looking at, they could be any one of those things.

If the things growing out of the top of the animal's head are made of bone, then they are antlers. Animals with antlers—male deer, moose, and elk or caribou of both sexes—grow new ones every year. This growth starts in the late spring. The branched antlers are well-developed by the end of May and are covered with velvet. This velvet is actually a layer of fur and skin, complete with blood vessels and nerves. Antlers continue to grow throughout the summer. When the antlers stop growing in August, the velvet begins to dry. The velvet dies and painlessly peels off, revealing the hardened antlers underneath. Animals keep these antlers through the winter. By spring, the antlers begin to separate from the skull and will eventually drop off.

Horns are made up of a very different substance than the bone of antlers. Usually, horns are hollow. They are made of keratin, the same substance that makes up your fingernails and hair. Like your hair and nails, horns are always growing, and just like a nail, if the point or tip of a horn breaks, it can grow back.

Animals such as the bighorn sheep develop growth rings on their horns each year. Most animals with horns—bison, bulls, cattle, and goats—have only two horns, each with one point. Like many other horned animals, the four-horned antelope has two horns between its ears. But it also has a pair of horns between the ridges of the skull above its eyes. An exception to the one-point rule is the pronghorn antelope. Its horns have two points. It is also an exception because it sheds its horns regularly. Probably the most famous horned animal doesn't really have a horn at all. The rhinoceros' horn is not a true horn. Its horn is solid and is made of dense hair packed together.

Horns grow out of the skull, but tusks are actually teeth growing out of the mouth. There are two types of deer that do not grow antlers: the Chinese water deer and the musk deer grow tusks instead. Other animals with tusks are warthogs, peccaries, walruses, narwhals, and elephants. One of the most extreme examples of tusks can be found in Asia on the babirusa, a kind of wild hog. This animal's tusks grow up through its snout and then curve around to make a complete circle, sometimes touching its forehead.

Unfortunately, many animals are killed or wounded each year for their horns or tusks. Some people grind horns or tusks into powder they can use to make traditional medicines. Others want the ivory to make jewelry or other decorations. This has led to many of these animals becoming threatened or endangered. Fortunately, there are alternatives to using ivory for jewelry. One of the most natural substitutes is the one animal part that can be renewed—antlers.

The next time you see an animal, ask yourself, "Do those things sticking out of its head have one point or many points?" "Are they growing from its mouth or from its skull?" With those answers, you should easily be able to identify if the animal has antlers, horns, or tusks.

Nonfiction Reading Comprehension • 5–6 © 2005 Creative Teaching Press

Name _____ Date _____

Animal Groups

aerie	ambush	army	kindle	knot
business	charm	clutter	pod	pride
crash	flock	gaggle	skulk	sleuth
labour	murder	nursery	bevy	rookery
	shiver	array	congress	

Fill in the blanks with the name for each group of animals. Use a dictionary if you need help.

1 hedgehogs __ __ __ __ __

2 hummingbirds __ __ __ __ __

3 moles __ __ __ __ __ __ __

4 raccoons __ __ __ __ __ __

5 geese __ __ __ __ __ __

6 eagles __ __ __ __ __

7 quail __ __ __ __ __

8 ravens __ __ __ __ __ __

9 caterpillars __ __ __ __

10 bears __ __ __ __ __

11 lions __ __ __ __

12 kittens __ __ __ __ __

13 frogs __ __ __ __

14 camels __ __ __ __ __ __

15 rhinoceros __ __ __ __ __

16 crows __ __ __ __ __ __

17 penguins __ __ __ __ __ __ __

18 cats __ __ __ __ __ __ __

19 ferrets __ __ __ __ __ __ __

20 whales __ __ __

21 sharks __ __ __ __ __ __

22 foxes __ __ __ __ __

23 tigers __ __ __ __ __ __

Nonfiction Reading Comprehension • 5–6 © 2005 Creative Teaching Press

Name _____ Date _____

Comparing Crowns

Write characteristics of antlers, horns, and tusks to complete the chart.

Antlers	Horns	Tusks

Nonfiction Reading Comprehension • 5–6 © 2005 Creative Teaching Press

Who's Who?

Write whether each animal has antlers, horns, or tusks.

1 _____

2 _____

3 _____

4 _____

5 _____

6 _____

Which Would You Want?

Write what you would like about having antlers, horns, and tusks to complete the chart.

Antlers	Horns	Tusks

Put a star by the one you would most want to have. Then finish the paragraph.

I would want to have _____ the most, because

_____

_____

_____

_____

_____

_____

_____

_____

_____

_____

_____

_____

_____

_____.

Math Is Math—Isn't It?

People around the world speak many different languages. If you opened up a math book in France or in the Netherlands, wouldn't you expect to see 2 + 2 = 4? Of course, two and two always adds up to four, but there are differences in the way people do math around the world.

If you look at the number **10.17**, you would read it as **ten and seventeen hundredths**. The period in the middle of the number is called the decimal point. It separates the whole number from the fraction. In some countries, like Brazil and Switzerland, you would not see a decimal point separating the whole number from the fraction. In these countries and in many others, students writing ten and seventeen hundredths would use a comma instead of a decimal point. It would look like this: **10,17**. You may be asking yourself what people in these countries do when they want to write a number greater than 999. We would use a comma to separate the hundreds from the thousands in a number. Since they are already using the comma to separate the whole number and the fraction, what do they do? It depends on the country. Some countries simply put a space, so fifty-two thousand five hundred sixty-seven looks like **52 567**. Others use a period, so it looks like this: **52.567**. Can you read this number: **9.279,8**? If you said nine thousand two hundred seventy-nine and eight tenths, then you understand how students in some other parts of the world write numbers.

Writing numbers is not the only thing that is different about math in other countries. Some number names don't mean the same thing. How much is a billion? You would probably say that it is one thousand times one million or **1,000,000,000**. Your peers in countries such as Australia and India would agree. However, if you went to a math class in Mexico or in Sweden, the answer would be different. In those countries and others—like Germany, Poland, and Colombia—a billion is one million times one million or **1,000,000,000,000**. They have different names for the number **1,000,000,000**, but all are similar to the word *miliardo* used in Italy or *milliarde* used in Austria.

Though the names for the numbers may be different, the countries mentioned all change number names every three digits. Even that is different in other parts of the world. In China and Japan, number names change every four digits. For example, in Japan 10,000 equals one *man* and at 100,000,000 it changes to one *oku*.

As people conduct business with others around the world, it becomes important to know the variations in how numbers are written in different countries. After all, if someone is ordering a billion bolts from your company, it is important to know if that is a one with nine zeros after it or if it is a thousand times more than that!

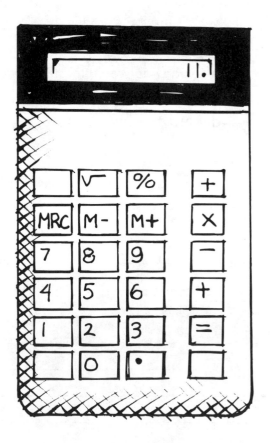

Nonfiction Reading Comprehension • 5–6 © 2005 Creative Teaching Press

Name _____ Date _____

Math Words

acute angle	area	chord	variable
circumference	diameter	equation	symmetry
equivalent fractions	factor	improper fraction	ray
inequality	mean	median	radius
mixed number	mode	obtuse angle	perimeter
parallel lines			

Match each example with a vocabulary word from the box. Write the word on the line. Use the glossary in your math book if you need help.

23 + 93 = 116 _____	A •———————→ B _____	4½ _____
36: 1, 2, 3, 4, 6, 9, 12, 18, 36 _____	**n** + 5 = _____	5 + 4 > 7 _____
 _____	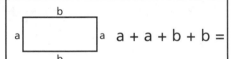 _____	 _____
76 87 Average = 85 92 _____	_____	$\frac{1}{2} = \frac{6}{12}$ _____
πr^2 _____	_____	_____
2, 3, 3, 5, **7, 7, 7**, 8, 9, 10, 10 _____	 _____	1, 5, 8, **11**, 13, 17, 23 _____
a[b] a × b = _____	$\frac{37}{5}$ _____	_____

A Letter to the World

Would you like everyone to use a comma or a decimal point in the same way, or would you rather that a billion meant the same thing worldwide? Choose an issue and write a letter to the world convincing them of your opinion. Use facts from the passage to support your argument.

_____

_____

_____

_____

People of the World
Every Street
Every City, Every Country

Dear People of the World,

_____

_____

_____

_____

_____

_____

_____

_____

_____

_____

_____

_____

Sincerely,

Nonfiction Reading Comprehension • 5–6 © 2005 Creative Teaching Press

How a Barometer Works

How does the weather forecaster on television know what the weather will be like tomorrow? One of the things the forecaster looks at is air pressure. Generally, if there is high pressure in the area, the weather will be clear. You can expect clouds or precipitation in an area of low pressure. How does the meteorologist know what the air pressure is? He or she uses an instrument called a barometer.

The first barometer was invented by a scientist named Evangelista Torricelli in 1643. At first, he tried to use water, but it was too difficult. His mentor, the scientist Galileo, suggested that he try mercury, which is fourteen times denser than water. To create his barometer, Torricelli took a 3-foot-long glass tube that was sealed at one end and filled it with mercury. The tube was heated to force the air out. Without allowing any air bubbles back in, Torricelli set the open end of the tube into a dish, called a cistern, with more mercury in it. When the mercury in the tube settled, it created a vacuum, or empty space, at the top of the tube. This amount of space would change as the air pressure changed. When there was greater air pressure, it pushed down on the mercury in the cistern, forcing mercury up the tube and making the vacuum smaller. When the air pressure was lower, the pressure from the vacuum was greater. That pushed the mercury down in the tube. Originally, this atmospheric pressure was measured in inches of mercury, according to its height in the tube.

There are problems with measuring atmospheric pressure with Torricelli's tube, however. It is not completely accurate. For example, atmospheric pressure decreases the higher the elevation, so if you were to measure the pressure at ground level and then climb a very tall building and measure again, you would get two different readings. This is because the pull or pressure from Earth's gravity is less the farther you get from the center of the planet. Also, it is not easy to carry around a 3-foot-long glass tube filled with mercury.

A more accurate type of barometer is the smaller aneroid barograph. An aneroid is a bellows made out of flexible metal. This bellows is a pleated tube or box that is sealed after some of the air is taken out. It can expand and contract up and down, according to the atmospheric pressure. Attached to the aneroid is a pen that marks a line on a slowly turning cylinder of paper. This barograph can record the barometric pressure for an entire week on one cylinder. Many aneroid barometers are attached to computers, which record the data and use it to make all kinds of charts and graphs about the changes in pressure. Some maps have lines, called isobars, drawn on them to join places that have the same pressure readings.

There is one more element, along with the barometric pressure, that helps the weather forecaster decide what the weather will be. The meteorologist also needs to know something about the direction the wind is coming from. Winds from the east, when combined with dropping barometric pressure, usually bring storms. Western winds can bring clearing and fair weather.

Listen carefully to the forecast. You now know that if you hear, "The winds are coming out of the northeast and the barometer is falling steadily," you will probably want to cancel your picnic. A prediction that, "A large area of high pressure is coming in from the west," however, probably means you can go ahead and make the sandwiches and lemonade.

Name _____ Date _____

Weather Words

Match each weather word to its definition.

1 _____ Wind-Chill Factor

2 _____ Tropical Storm

3 _____ Dew Point

4 _____ Humidity

5 _____ Trough

6 _____ Heat Index

7 _____ Alberta Clipper

8 _____ Jet Stream

9 _____ Bermuda High

10 _____ Tropical Depression

11 _____ Cloud Base

12 _____ Lake Effect

13 _____ Virga

14 _____ Nor'easter

a. a winter storm coming out of Alberta, Canada, that is fast-moving and often has high winds.

b. an area of high pressure over Bermuda that causes warm weather over the eastern United States

c. the level of the atmosphere at which clouds become visible

d. how cool the air must be for there to be dew

e. a calculation using temperature and relative humidity that tells how hot it "feels"

f. how much water vapor is in the air

g. narrow bands of high-speed winds usually found above fronts

h. the way a lake, usually one of the Great Lakes, affects the climate around it, especially the snowfall

i. a strong wind or storm from the northeast

j. a long area of low pressure

k. precipitation that evaporates before hitting the ground

l. a calculation using temperature and wind speed that tells how cold it "feels"

m. an area of tropical low pressure with little wind

n. an area of tropical low pressure with very strong winds

Nonfiction Reading Comprehension • 5–6 © 2005 Creative Teaching Press

Name _____ Date _____

Build Your Own Barometer

To make a barometer you will need:
- a small coffee can
- plastic wrap
- a rubber band
- a drinking straw cut to a point on one end
- tape
- a piece of paper

Instructions
1. Stretch the plastic wrap tightly across the open end of the coffee can and secure it with the rubber band.
2. Put the straw on top of the plastic wrap with the pointed end hanging off and the other end at about the middle of the plastic wrap. Tape the straw in place.
3. Place your barometer someplace where it will not heat up, or you will not get accurate pressure readings.
4. Tape the paper in place behind your barometer. Mark where the point of the straw is on the paper.
5. Check your barometer from time to time and see if the point of the straw is pointing higher or lower than before.

Use information you read in the passage to help explain how your barometer works.

1 Why do you use plastic wrap instead of a material such as fabric or cardboard?

2 Could you use a large piece of rubber from a balloon instead of the plastic wrap?

3 Why can't you put your barometer where it will get hot?

4 If the point of the straw goes higher than where you started, is the pressure rising or falling? Explain.

5 If the point of the straw goes lower than where you started, is the pressure rising or falling? Explain.

Name _____ Date _____

Predicting the Weather

Use the table with information from the National Weather Service to answer the questions.

Wind	Barometer	Conditions
SW to NW	high pressure and steady	Fair with slight temperature change for one to two days
SW to NW	high pressure and rising rapidly	Fair, followed within two days by rain
SW to NW	high pressure and stationary	Continued fair, with no decided temperature change
SW to NW	high pressure and falling slowly	Slowly rising temperature and fair for two days
S to SE	high pressure and falling slowly	Rain within 24 hours
S to SE	high pressure and falling rapidly	Wind increasing in force, and rain within 12 to 24 hours
SE to NE	high pressure and falling slowly	Rain in 12 to 18 hours
SE to NE	high pressure and falling rapidly	Increasing wind, and rain within 12 hours
E to NE	high pressure and falling slowly	In summer, with light winds, rain may not fall for several days. In winter, rain within 24 hours
E to NE	high pressure and falling rapidly	In summer, rain probably within 12 to 24 hours. In winter, rain or snow, with increasing winds, will often set in when the barometer begins to fall and the wind sets in from the NE
SE to NE	medium pressure and falling slowly	Rain will continue one to two days. SE to NE, 30.00 or below and falling rapidly—Rain, with high wind, followed, within 36 hours by clearing, and in winter by colder air
S to SW	medium pressure and rising slowly	Clearing within a few hours, and fair for several days
S to E	low pressure and falling rapidly	Severe storm imminent, followed within 24 hours by clearing, and in winter by colder air
E to N	low pressure and falling rapidly	Severe northeast gale and heavy precipitation; in winter, heavy snow, followed by a cold wave
Going to W	low pressure and rising rapidly	Clearing and colder

1 On July 3, Paul hears the following weather report: "Winds are from the northeast. The barometer is falling rapidly." Are the fireworks and parade likely to be rained out?

2 Grace is packing to go camping for the weekend. The weather report says, "The barometer is rising slowly with winds from the south." Does Grace need to be sure to pack her raingear?

3 Josie wants to plant a new rosebush. For it to grow well, it should receive rain within three days of planting. The weather report says that the barometer is rising rapidly with winds blowing from the southwest to the northwest. Should she plant her new rosebush today?

Nonfiction Reading Comprehension • 5–6 © 2005 Creative Teaching Press

World Climate Zones

Weather is what is happening wherever you are. Is it sunny? Is it raining? Is the wind blowing? Climate is different than weather. Climate is what kind of weather a place has over a long period of time—at least thirty years, in fact.

Two important parts of climate are how much precipitation—rain, sleet, or snow—there is and what the usual temperatures are. The climate of an area determines what kinds of animals and plants can live there and what human beings must do to survive there, too. The earth has six climate zones. They are dry or arid, high elevation or mountain, Mediterranean, polar, temperate, and tropical.

Arid or dry climates are usually hot all year, but the temperature in a single day can vary widely. Desert temperatures may reach well over one hundred degrees during the day, but without clouds to hold the heat in, nights can get very cold. Steppes are included in this zone, too. Steppes are large areas of land in southeastern Europe or Asia that have no trees and receive little rain. They don't look like the sandy deserts we think of when we imagine a dry climate.

Not all classification systems recognize high elevation or mountain climate zones since they can be found within any of the other zones. Because of their extreme altitude, mountain zones are cold all year. This is because air is less dense at higher altitudes and has a harder time holding heat. The climate of Mount Everest is always extremely cold, even in the summertime.

A Mediterranean climate is characterized by hot, dry summers. The winters, however, are very mild and pleasant. The climate within the Mediterranean zone can vary depending on how close an area is to water. Land heats up and cools off faster than water. The temperatures on the coast tend to stay about the same. Inland, it will be hotter in summer and cooler in winter.

It is very cold and dry all year long in the polar climate zones. Many people don't know that Antarctica is so dry that it actually qualifies as a desert! Near the earth's poles, the sun's rays are hitting at such an angle that little warming radiation is received. Temperatures are above freezing only about four months out of the year. This climate zone is characterized by permafrost and tundra. Only the top layer of soil thaws out in the tundra. Beneath it the permafrost is always frozen. The growing season is short, so plants are small and no trees grow.

If you live in a place that has cold winters and mild summers, then you live in a temperate climate zone. Much of the United States falls within this zone, which stretches from the tropics to the polar regions. One large part of this climate zone is the taiga. This area is made up mostly of pine and fir forests. The nights are long and cold in winter. The days are long and humid in summer. Deciduous forests, with trees whose leaves change with the seasons, are also part of the temperate zone, as are temperate, coastal rain forests. Not all areas of the temperate zone are covered in trees, however. Wide grasslands, or prairies, cover other parts of this climate zone, mostly in the middle section of the United States. Africa, Asia, and South America have temperate grasslands as well.

The final zone is the tropical zone. Here it is hot and wet year-round. This rain comes from the collision near the equator of Northern Hemisphere winds blowing from the northeast and Southern Hemisphere winds blowing from the southeast. When they meet, the air is forced upwards. As it cools, clouds and rain are produced. Temperatures are hotter at the equator because that part of the earth receives more of the sun's direct rays.

No matter where you live, the climate affects you. As you travel throughout your own climate zone or to other zones, you may come to appreciate the differences in climate.

Name _____ Date _____

Climate Words

Unscramble the words to complete each sentence.

1. In the **cialport** zone, it is hot and rainy all year long. _____

2. The climate in a **Manrtdeirneae** zone is affected by how close an area is to water.
_____

3. If you live in the **pemraette** zone, you are used to cold winters and mild summers.
_____

4. The **utmeptareer** means how hot or cold it is. _____

5. Take an umbrella in case of **ciitiponrepta.** _____

6. If you can't dig deeply because the soil is frozen, you are in the **draunt**.
_____

7. If you are in a cool, pine forest, you may be in the **agait.** _____

8. The earth is divided into two **phimershees.** _____

9. The middle of the United States is covered by **glandsssar.** _____

10. You will find **froapmerts** under the soil in polar climate zones. _____

11. The higher the **levantioe** the colder the temperature. _____

12. In the **eterds,** days are very hot, but nights can get cold. _____

13. Places that do not receive much rain are **dria.** _____

14. The sun shines the most light on the **roquate.** _____

15. A large area of land in Europe or Asia that has no trees is called a **pestep.**
_____

Nonfiction Reading Comprehension • 5–6 © 2005 Creative Teaching Press

Matching Zones

Write the climate zone shown in each picture.

 1 _____

 2 _____

 3 _____

 4 _____

5 _____

6 _____

7 _____

8 _____

What's Wrong with This Picture?

Describe what is wrong in each picture.

_____

_____

_____

_____

_____

_____

_____

_____

_____

_____

_____

_____

_____

_____

_____

_____

_____

_____

_____

_____

_____

_____

_____

_____

_____

_____

_____

Name _____ Date _____

My Zone

Draw a picture of your climate zone in the box.

```
┌─────────────────────────────────────────────────────────────────┐
│                                                                   │
│                                                                   │
│                                                                   │
│                                                                   │
│                                                                   │
│                                                                   │
│                                                                   │
│                                                                   │
│                                                                   │
│                                                                   │
│                                                                   │
└─────────────────────────────────────────────────────────────────┘
```

Finish the paragraph below by writing about your climate zone.

I live in a _____ climate zone. The winters are
_____ and the summers are
_____. My favorite part of living in the
_____ climate zone is _____
_____. I don't like
_____
_____. If I could visit
another climate zone, I would go to the _____ zone, because
_____
_____
_____
_____.

Plate Tectonics

Why do we have earthquakes? Is California going to fall into the ocean one day? How can there be similar fossils on continents on opposite sides of the Atlantic Ocean? The answers to these questions and to many more can be explained by the theory of plate tectonics.

Tectonics comes from the Greek word *tekon,* which means "builder." The theory is that the earth's surface is built from about a dozen large plates of solid rock that float on the molten, or liquid, surface below. Like a hard boiled egg, the earth has three layers: the thin, hard crust; the semi-solid mantle; and the core. Like the egg's shell, the earth's crust can crack, and once cracked, it can slide around on the layer beneath. Sometime in the far distant past, this sliding of the earth's crust occurred. Exactly what caused these plates to slide, we still don't know for certain, but we do know that they began moving several billion years ago. They have been very slowly moving over and around the earth ever since. Sometimes they bump into one another. Other times they drift apart. Occasionally, one plate ends up getting trapped underneath another one. Let's look at what happens during each of these events.

Imagine two cars driving toward each other. If they hit head-on, what will happen? The front ends will crumple up. The same thing happened when tectonic plates collided long ago. One example of colliding plates is the Himalayan mountains—the highest mountains in the world.

Have you ever looked carefully at a map of the world? Sometimes it looks like a big jigsaw puzzle. You may have noticed that South America would fit very nicely next to Africa. Back in 1596, a mapmaker named Abraham Ortelius noticed this very thing. He thought that the Americas must have once been attached to Africa and to Europe but something caused them to drift apart. Scientific evidence now shows that tectonic plates do move apart from each other. This is because new crust is always being formed deep within the ocean. The Mid-Atlantic Ridge is where the new crust that pushes Europe and North America apart from each other is formed.

If new crust is always being formed, why doesn't the earth keep getting bigger and bigger? It is because of the last thing mentioned above. Sometimes one plate gets forced beneath another plate. Several of these convergent boundaries are in the Pacific Ocean. This subduction of one plate underneath another causes earthquakes and volcanoes. The "ring of fire" is used to describe the area around the Pacific Ocean that has a lot of volcanoes because of these convergent boundaries. Also, earthquakes are more common in areas closer to the Pacific Ocean. Mountains can also be formed by the subduction of one plate under another. The South American Andes are an example of this.

Sometimes tectonic plates just slide past one another. Probably the best-known example of this kind of plate movement is the San Andreas Fault in California. The land to the west of this fault is moving to the northwest at a rate of about 5 centimeters a year. As far as anyone can tell, this has been happening for the past ten million years. Even if a catastrophic earthquake did occur along this fault line, California would not fall into the ocean. The plate it is on would continue to move across the mantle of the earth as it has for billions of years.

As scientific technology improves, we find new ways to learn about the movement of the earth's crust. We may never know all of the answers, but the knowledge we are gaining allows us to better predict when the movement of the plates will cause earthquakes and volcanic eruptions. This will help to save lives as we go about living on this ever-changing earth.

Nonfiction Reading Comprehension • 5–6 © 2005 Creative Teaching Press

Name _____ Date _____

"Geo" Means Earth

Many of our words have Greek or Latin roots, especially scientific words. The word ending *-ology* means "thoughts about a subject" or "exchange of ideas." The word *geology* then means "thoughts and ideas about the earth." People often say it is the study of the earth.

Match each *-ology* word with the subject it covers. Use a dictionary if you need help.

1 ___ biology

2 ___ cardiology

3 ___ cryptology

4 ___ dermatology

5 ___ entomology

6 ___ gerontology

7 ___ graphology

8 ___ hematology

9 ___ hydrology

10 ___ ichthyology

11 ___ kinesiology

12 ___ neurology

13 ___ pathology

14 ___ phonology

15 ___ physiology

16 ___ psychology

17 ___ topology

18 ___ zoology

a. old age

b. movement

c. sound

d. writing

e. living things

f. insects

g. fish

h. water

i. secret codes

j. animal life

k. skin

l. heart

m. place

n. mind

o. body processes

p. blood

q. disease

r. nerves

What Makes Them Move?

Cross out the statements that are not about things that would cause the tectonic plates to move.

1 New crust is being formed in the Mid-Atlantic Ridge.

2 In 1912, Alfred Lothar Wegener came up with the theory of Continental Drift.

3 Similar fossils are found in Africa and in Antarctica.

4 The layer under the crust of the earth is semi-solid.

5 Off the coast of Washington and Oregon, the Juan de Fuca plate is sinking below the North American plate.

6 Rocks in the ocean are much younger than rocks on the continents.

7 The Earth's magnetic poles have switched back and forth over time.

8 Magma pushes up through cracks in the earth's crust.

9 The Marianas Trench is the deepest place on earth.

10 The mantle is heated by the core of the earth and then moves upward toward the crust in a circular motion.

Nonfiction Reading Comprehension • 5–6 © 2005 Creative Teaching Press

Name _____ Date _____

What's Going On?

Describe what is happening in each illustration.

_____
_____
_____
_____
_____
_____
_____
_____
_____
_____

_____
_____
_____
_____
_____
_____
_____
_____
_____
_____
_____
_____
_____

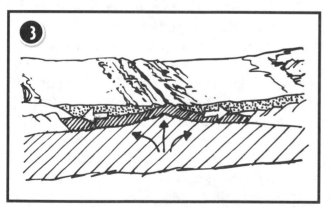

_____
_____
_____
_____
_____
_____
_____
_____

_____
_____
_____
_____
_____
_____
_____

Happy New Year!

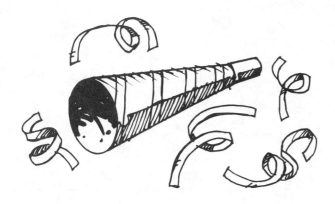

S Novim Godom! Prospero Año Nuevo! Buon Capodanno! Whatever the language, it is a happy new year. Celebrating the beginning of a new year goes back 4,000 years to ancient Babylon. At that time, spring was the time to celebrate. That made sense because so many things come to life in the spring. Around 100 B.C., when the Romans created a new calendar, the celebration was changed to January first. Many cultures have adopted this date for the celebration.

Food is an important part of many New Year's celebrations. Some people eat sauerkraut or other forms of cabbage to increase their prosperity in the coming year. Eating pork or ham is also thought to bring prosperity. In some parts of the United States, black-eyed peas are eaten for luck. In Brazil, they eat lentils. Other people think eating rice brings good fortune. Some cultures prepare cakes or breads with coins in them. The person who finds the coin will have good luck and prosperity in the year ahead. In Spain and Portugal, people eat twelve grapes as the clock chimes for twelve happy months ahead. Finally, some people eat donuts or cakes made in the shape of a ring to symbolize the year coming full circle. In Germany, they leave a portion of each food on their plates until after midnight. This is supposed to ensure that there will be enough food in the year ahead.

Many New Year's traditions come down from ancient times when evil spirits were driven away before another year began. In many places, people set off fireworks or other explosions, or they bang pots and pans together. In other locations, they ring church bells. In the Netherlands, they burn their Christmas trees in bonfires.

Friendship is an important part of many New Year's celebrations. People often gather in friends' homes, at parties or dances, or even in the streets of large cities, like the annual Big Apple drop in New York City's Times Square. Many people visit friends and family on New Year's Day. In some places, it is very important that the right person be the very first visitor of the new year as it brings either prosperity or bad luck to the home depending on who puts their foot through the door first. Most people would not like to find a big pile of broken dishes on the doorstep on New Year's Day, but in Denmark it is a sign that you have many friends. Children especially like to go visiting on New Year's Day in some countries because it is the tradition to give them special treats and money.

Making a fresh start is another important way many people mark the start of a new year. In some places, they burn people made of straw to show that they are getting rid of bad habits. In some cultures, houses are given a thorough cleaning. In others, water is sprinkled around as a symbol of cleansing. For some, it is traditional to clean up the entire town by collecting trash and litter. Be careful not to take things out of your house, however. You may take the good luck out with them. At least, that is what some cultures believe. In other locations, people buy or make new clothes. Many people make resolutions, or ways they hope to improve themselves in the coming year. They may decide to lose weight or to not fight with their brothers and sisters. Their resolutions may not last long, but they feel good about making them.

No matter how you chose to celebrate the new year, it is a time of new beginnings. It is an opportunity to try to be a better person—both to yourself and to others. How will you try to improve?

Nonfiction Reading Comprehension • 5–6 © 2005 Creative Teaching Press

Name _____ Date _____

New Words

We often use a lot of old, tired words in our writing. Find some new ways to say what you really mean. Use a thesaurus to find some alternatives to these overused words.

Old Word	New Words
said	
good	
nice	
go	
sad	

Write five sentences, using a new word from each group.

1. _____

2. _____

3. _____

4. _____

5. _____

Not Just January First

Although many cultures celebrate the new year on the first day of January, many others do not. Non-Christian cultures celebrate according to their own religious beliefs. Other cultures use different calendars, so their new year celebrations fall on different dates from those on the Gregorian calendar that most of the Western world uses.

Use different colored crayons to color in the boxes on the map key on the New Year Map page. Use the corresponding colors to shade in the countries on the map according to when they celebrate the beginning of a new year.

- In Burma, the coming of the new year is based on a fixed zodiac. It falls between the thirteenth and sixteenth of April.

- In Cambodia and Laos, they use the lunar calendar, so the new year begins about the twelfth of April.

- Diwali is the New Year's celebration for people living in Gujarat, India. It occurs in October or November.

- The people of Hong Kong, Malaysia, and Singapore celebrate the new year at the same time as the Chinese, in January or February.

- Most Iranians are Muslims. The Muslim calendar is lunar based, and the year has only 354 days. All Muslim holidays are then eleven days earlier than the year before.

- In Sri Lanka, they use the Hindu calendar and celebrate the new year in April.

- April is also the time for New Year's celebrations in Thailand.

- The people of Pakistan celebrate the new year in March. They call it Nawrooz, or New Day.

- The Vietnamese New Year is celebrated on the first night of the first moon after the sun enters Aquarius. This falls in January or February.

New Year Map

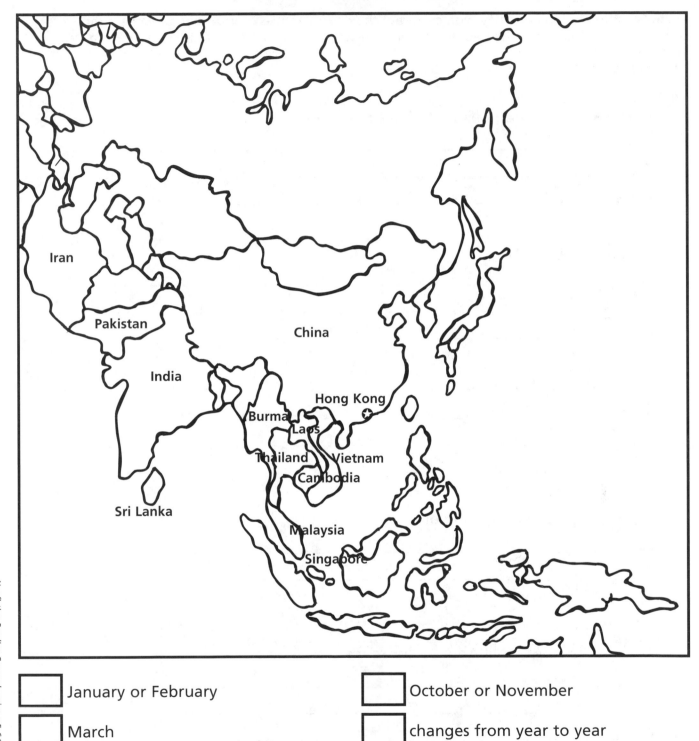

☐ January or February   ☐ October or November

☐ March   ☐ changes from year to year

☐ mid-April

Name _____ Date _____

My New Year

Complete the outline with ways you celebrate the new year. Use your outline to write a short essay about how you celebrate the beginning of a new year. You can add more details to each paragraph, if necessary.

I.   Introduction: When I Celebrate New Year's

    A. day _____

    B. time _____

    C. for how long _____

II. Special Foods I Eat

    A. _____

    B. _____

    C. _____

III. Traditions That I Observe

    A. _____

    B. _____

    C. _____

IV. Ways I Prepare for a New Beginning

    A. _____

    B. _____

    C. _____

V.   Conclusion: How I Feel About New Year's

    A. _____

    B. _____

    C. _____

Nonfiction Reading Comprehension • 5–6 © 2005 Creative Teaching Press

Ramadan and Eid al-Fitr

The month of Ramadan and the celebration of Eid al-Fitr at its end are very important to Muslims, people who practice the Islamic faith. About ten million Muslims live in the United States, and there are over a billion followers throughout the world.

Unlike most Western holidays that fall at the same time every year, the time of Islamic holidays in relation to the seasons changes from year to year. This is because the Islamic calendar is based on the lunar year and has only 354 days. Muslims will be thirty-two years old before they celebrate a holiday twice on the same date (on the Gregorian calendar). The new month cannot begin until someone trusted by the community sees the new moon and declares the beginning of the month. Most of the Muslim world follows the declaration made in Saudi Arabia. People begin looking for the new moon on the twenty-ninth day. If it is seen, the new month begins. If not, then the month continues for another day, and a new month begins after the thirtieth day.

Ramadan is the ninth month of the Islamic calendar. It is a month of fasting, not eating from sunup until sundown, and doing good deeds. Eid al-Fitr is a celebration marking the end of the fast and is celebrated on the first three days of Shawal, the tenth month. It is one of the two most important celebrations in the Islamic faith. The three days are spent focusing on all of the blessings that Allah, God, has given them. It is a time of great joy and thanksgiving.

Just before the beginning of Eid, many people decorate their houses. Muslims get up very early on the first day of Eid. They take a bath and put on all brand-new clothes, including shoes. They may have a sweet snack, such as dates. Then they gather in a large, open area about an hour after sunrise to say very special prayers, called Salatul Eid. After prayers, they go home to eat a special breakfast. It is the first meal they have been able to eat during the daylight hours in a month.

Most children don't receive gifts for Eid. It is the custom, however, for visitors to give children money, usually brand-new bills or coins, on the first two days of the celebration. Children enjoy collecting this money because there are often carnivals or fairs during Eid, where they can buy candy or toys or take a turn on the rides.

Many friends and family members visit during Eid. The visits usually begin around the middle of the morning with friends and neighbors. Special cakes are served at each visit.

Dinnertime is spent with family. Each day a different part of the family visits so everyone gets to spend time together. After dinner, more visits can be made. At each visit, there are greetings of "Eid Saeed" or "Eid Mubarak," which mean "Happy Holidays" or "Blessed Eid."

Another important part of Eid is almsgiving, providing money for the poor. After fasting during Ramadan, Muslims are more aware of what it is to be hungry like the poor. Muslims choose to pay a kind of tax for each person in the family. This food or money helps the less fortunate to celebrate Eid as well. Helping others is another way to celebrate what they have.

The celebration of Eid is about being grateful for all one has and about trying to do what is right. It is a time to forget bad feelings toward others. Muslims are observing the fact that they have just spent a month becoming closer to Allah and wish to maintain that closeness.

Nonfiction Reading Comprehension • 5–6 © 2005 Creative Teaching Press

Name _____ Date _____

My Favorite Holiday

Fill in the Venn diagram with things about your favorite holiday that are the same as or different from Eid al-Fitr. Use your completed diagram to write a brief essay comparing your favorite holiday with Eid. If Eid is your favorite holiday, compare the similarities and differences between Ramadan and Eid.

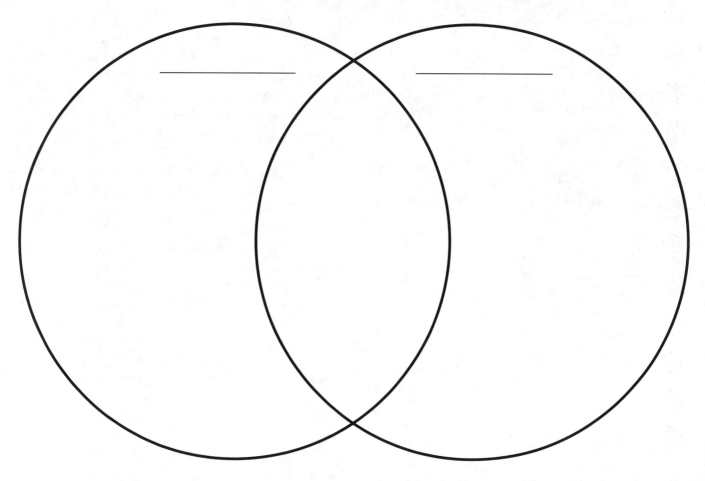

Name _____ Date _____

Would You?

Look at the list of activities. Circle any activities that someone would do to get ready for or do during Eid al-Fitr.

1 Go to the bank

2 Send out party invitations

3 Ride a merry-go-round

4 Go shopping for new clothes

5 Decorate a tree

6 Set the alarm clock

7 Fight with your sister

8 Think about all of the good things you have

9 Buy a new car

10 Do something nice for someone

11 Paint the house

12 Hire a deejay

13 Learn special prayers

14 Do some baking

15 Light candles

One the lines below, tell why someone would not do the things you did not circle.

#_____ _____

#_____ _____

#_____ _____

#_____ _____

#_____ _____

#_____ _____

#_____ _____

The Silk Road

The Silk Road was not a single road, and it was not made of silk. It was a series of trade routes across Asia that stretched over four thousand miles, connecting the Western civilizations, such as the Greeks and Persians, with the Eastern civilizations of the Chinese. Trade began during the second century, or perhaps even earlier, and continued for hundreds of years until transportation by ship became a safer option around the 1400s.

Many goods were transported over the Silk Road. It was silk that originally fueled the development of this trade, however. The Romans were very interested in this beautiful, soft fabric, which was very different from the wools and linens they were used to. Eventually, silk only accounted for a small portion of the goods traded. Merchants took coral, glass, gems, gold, ivory, precious metals, and textiles eastward to China. They also brought rare plants and animals such as falcons, gazelles, hunting dogs, leopards, lions, ostriches, parrots, and peacocks. Traveling westward were traders with bronze, ceramics, cinnamon and other spices, furs, iron, jade, lacquer, tea, and even rhubarb.

Traveling this route was very dangerous for the caravans. Parts of the Great Wall of China were built to help protect the travelers on what would later become the Silk Road. Harsh weather conditions are found along much of the Silk Road, from scorching deserts to freezing mountain passes. Travelers also had to worry about having enough water in this arid part of the world. Blinding sandstorms could strand caravans for days. Crossing high mountains could lead to altitude sickness. Probably the greatest danger faced by those traveling the Silk Road was bandits. The wealth of merchandise being carried across uninhabited lands was very tempting to those who chose to rob these traveling merchants. A single camel could carry up to five hundred pounds of trade goods. To avoid thieves, caravans banded together and hired armed guards. As many as one thousand camels might be grouped together for the journey. Chances were good, however, that not all the members of the caravan would survive the trip.

Very few traders traveled the whole route as it took over a year to go just one way. In fact, there are no records of Chinese businessmen making it to Europe. Usually, merchants ventured only part of the way and then sold their goods to other traders. A single item might pass through the hands of many different traders before reaching its final destination. Many goods never made it to the end of the route, ending up somewhere in the middle of Asia instead.

Trade goods were not the only things that passed along the Silk Road. Religion, especially Buddhism, was spread along this corridor as well. Technology was also shared. The Silk Road brought glass-making to China and paper-making to the West. Unfortunately, disease was also transmitted along the Silk Road. The bubonic plague that would eventually devastate Europe originally moved westward along the Silk Road.

Probably the most famous traveler on the Silk Road was Italian explorer Marco Polo. He was only seventeen years old in 1271 when he made the trek all the way east to present-day Beijing, China. He returned to Italy in 1295 with many interesting tales to tell about his travels.

There is no doubt that the history of the Silk Road is tied to the history of much of the world's cultures. The exchange of ideas and goods along this trade corridor had effects that have lasted to the present day. Our civilization owes much to those brave adventurers who sought to become wealthy through trade along the Silk Road.

Nonfiction Reading Comprehension • 5–6 © 2005 Creative Teaching Press

Finding Your Way

altitudes	arid	bandits	caravans	civilizations
goods	merchandise	merchants	rhubarb	technology
textiles	trade routes	transported	trek	uninhabited

Use the words from the box to complete the sentences.

1 The Silk Road was a collection of _____ across Asia.

2 Eastern and Western _____ traded with each other.

3 _____ hoped to trade and make money.

4 Some of the trade _____ were ivory and spices.

5 _____ is another word for fabrics.

6 Camels, horses, and donkeys _____ the goods.

7 It was a long and dangerous _____ along the Silk Road.

8 Traders traveled together in _____.

9 The merchants needed protection from _____.

10 Snow and sickness were a problem at high _____.

11 The _____ land did not provide much water.

12 Thieves tried to steal the valuable _____.

13 A plant that came to the West from China was _____.

14 Much of the land the merchants traveled through was _____.

15 Knowledge of how to make glass, or the _____, came to China from the West.

Nonfiction Reading Comprehension • 5–6 © 2005 Creative Teaching Press

Name _____ Date _____

Changing History

Fill in the missing causes and effects to complete the chart.

Cause	Effect
1 The Romans liked silk.	
2	Cities sprang up along the route in places where there were good supplies of water.
3	Only goods that could make a large profit were traded.
4 Bandits liked to rob the merchants.	
5	The Chinese learned to make glass.
6	Europeans learned more about Chinese culture.
7	Merchants only took their goods part of the way along the route.
8 Sailing became a safer and easier method of transporting goods.	
9 Buddhist missionaries traveled the Silk Road.	
10 Sandstorms were blinding.	

Buddhism became an important religion in China.
It took over a year to make the entire journey.
It was hard to find water in the arid lands.
Marco Polo wrote a book about his travels.
Technology traveled eastward over the Silk Road.

The journey had a lot of risks and dangers.
The Silk Road became a popular trade route.
Traders banded together in caravans.
Travelers got stranded.
Use of the Silk Road as a trade route declined.

Nonfiction Reading Comprehension • 5–6 © 2005 Creative Teaching Press

Does It Matter?

Cross out any events that would not affect trade on the Silk Road.

1. The name Silk Road was made up by Ferdinand von Richthofen in the 1800s.

2. Local people acted as guides along the most dangerous parts of the routes.

3. Dunhuang, a city along the Silk Road, has lots of beautiful Buddhist artwork.

4. Genghis Khan began conquering a large part of Asia in 1206.

5. Marco Polo did a lot of traveling in China before returning to Italy.

6. In the late 1800s and early 1900s, archaeologists dug up artifacts from the Silk Road.

7. People believed the Magi traveled the Silk Road on their way to see the baby Jesus.

8. The Jade Gate was a landmark along the route.

9. Bridges and paved roads were built along parts of the trade route.

10. Nestorian Christians escaped persecution by traveling east along the Silk Road.

11. The Sogdian people were the main "middlemen" or "go-betweens" for traders.

12. People believed that the deserts were inhabited by demons at night.

13. Two-hump, Bactrian camels were better than one-hump, dromedary camels.

14. The dunes of the Taklamakan Desert are always shifting.

15. The Chinese wanted gold.

Black Death

From the 1300s until the 1600s, people around the world lived in fear of outbreaks of a deadly disease. This disease could kill with amazing speed or could cause people to linger in unbearable pain. It caused people to abandon their loved ones and businesses to come to a halt. Even in modern times, its name brings to mind something terrible. It was the bubonic plague, also known as the Black Death.

The plague first arrived in Europe in October of 1347, when an Italian ship docked in Sicily. The merchants on board had recently returned from a trip to the Black Sea at the western end of the Silk Road. The disease had spread across the famous trade route from China. When they arrived, some crew members were already very ill with the disease. Before the Italians could be sent from the city, the disease had already spread. In less than a year, the plague had spread all the way to England. In the years of the European epidemic between 1347 and 1352, twenty-five million people, a third of the population, died of the plague. Some large cities lost more than half of their populations at rates of 500 to 800 people a day. It had taken nearly two hundred years for the population to grow from 50 million to 75 million and it took only five years to bring it back down to 50 million again.

All of this death had a negative effect on medieval society. There were two main ways people dealt with the threat of the plague. Some decided that if life was going to be short, they were going to live it up. Others sought to escape the plague by cutting off all contact with the outside world. Often those who were supposed to uphold the laws were dead or too ill to do so. There was a shortage of laborers. There were not enough people to harvest the crops or tend to the animals, some of which caught the plague, also. Houses and even entire villages were abandoned forever in an attempt to escape the disease. The Church had been an important part of everyday life, but now some people began to lose faith in the face of unanswered prayers for safety from the disease. Jews in some places found themselves being blamed for the disease.

Doctors in the Middle Ages were not successful in treating the plague. A group of French scientists studying the problem determined that the plague was caused by astrological forces combined with earthquakes. It wasn't until 1894 that the true cause of the plague was discovered—fleas. Actually, the plague mainly affected rats and other rodents. The fleas bit the rats and became infected themselves. In the flea, the plague bacteria kept blood, the flea's food source, from getting to its stomach. The hungry flea kept biting and biting, trying to fill up. Instead, the bites transmited the bacteria into all of its victims. In plague victims, a black sore would develop around the flea bite. Flu-like symptoms would develop and the lymph nodes would swell to the size of eggs. These swellings were called buboes and is where the name bubonic plague comes from. Purple spots would appear on the skin that would later turn black. In the end, the victim's nervous system would shut down, causing extreme pain and bizarre behavior before death. There was an additional form of the plague that was transmitted by people coughing. This pneumonic plague caused death much more quickly, which was fortunate since it caused people to have severe chest pains, coughing up blood, and hands and feet turned black.

The plague will always be around. In the United States, there were 390 reported cases of the plague between 1947 and 1996. Most were in the western states. Advances in technology make it easier to control rat populations and to get rid of fleas. Treatment with antibiotics has greatly reduced the death rate for those infected. Hopefully, with proper precautions, the world will never have to worry about another catastrophic outbreak of the plague.

Nonfiction Reading Comprehension • 5–6 © 2005 Creative Teaching Press

Name _____ Date _____

Synonym Search

affliction	bane	calamity	carnage	catastrophe
cataclysm	curse	decimation	disaster	epidemic
infestation	pestilence	scourge	tragedy	vexation

Find these synonyms for **plague** in the word search.

```
B  A  N  P  E  S  T  I  L  E  N  C  E
E  C  A  T  A  C  L  Y  S  M  E  C  B
M  A  F  C  A  R  N  A  G  E  N  U  A
I  N  F  E  S  T  A  T  I  O  N  R  N
C  A  L  A  M  I  T  Y  X  F  E  S  E
D  C  I  S  I  T  A  D  I  O  N  E  V
I  N  C  A  T  A  S  T  R  O  P  H  E
S  S  T  R  A  G  E  D  Y  S  M  E  X
A  C  I  R  S  E  R  C  A  T  A  C  A
S  C  O  U  R  G  E  E  N  T  F  F  T
T  U  N  R  Y  M  E  X  A  L  I  T  I
E  R  E  P  I  D  E  M  I  C  R  O  O
R  S  E  D  E  C  I  M  A  T  I  O  N
```

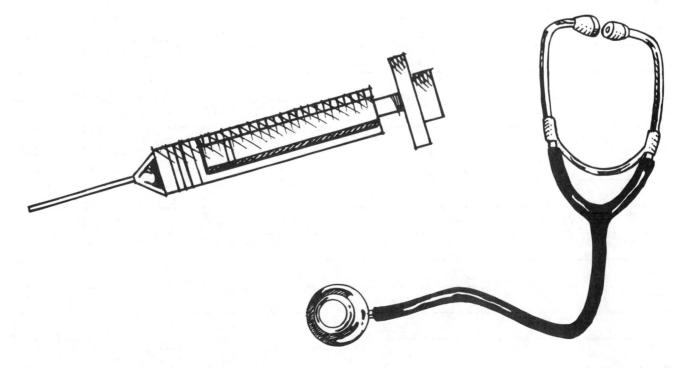

Staying Healthy

Dear Dr. Medieval,

    Recently there have been outbreaks of the plague in my country. I do not want to catch the disease. How can I keep myself healthy?

Sincerely,

Jane Peasant

Use the information from the passage to write an advice column for Dr. Medieval.

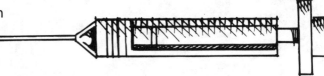

Dear Jane,

    If you want to avoid catching the plague, the first thing you should do is _____

_____

_____

_____

_____

_____

_____

_____

_____

_____

_____

_____

_____

_____

_____

_____

_____

Nonfiction Reading Comprehension • 5–6 © 2005 Creative Teaching Press

Ring Around the Rosie

Some people think the nursery rhyme "Ring Around the Rosie" describes parts of the Black Plague. Though there is no proof that the rhyme is that old, and there are many variations that have nothing to do with disease, people have invented connections.

Match each part of the rhyme with the meaning that has been attributed to it.

1 _____ Ring around the rosie

2 _____ A pocket full of posies

3 _____ Ashes, ashes

4 _____ We all fall down.

a. Most people died.

b. The smell from the dead and dying was so bad that people carried fragrant flowers to try to avoid the stench. If they were lucky enough to include fleabane in their bouquet, they might help avoid the plague. Another explanation is that people carried flowers to ward off the evil spirits they thought carried the disease.

c. Two explanations: Ashes is like "Achoo!" which would represent the sneezes of those infected with pneumonic plague. Ashes were what was left after houses or bodies were burned in an attempt to stop the disease from spreading.

d. Rose-colored spots occurred on the bodies of the victims. Also, black rings appeared around the flea bites, which were small, red bumps.

Nonfiction Reading Comprehension • 5–6 © 2005 Creative Teaching Press

York

Can you imagine turning twelve years old and all of a sudden having your best friend become your master? This is what happened to a boy named York. York was a slave, and his friend and master was one of the most famous men in history, William Clark. York would accompany Meriwether Lewis and Clark on one of the most amazing journeys in history.

York was born in 1771 or 1772 in Caroline County, Virginia. His parents, Old York and Rose, were the slaves of John Clark, William's father. Because William was only a year older, he and York became good friends as children—playing, exploring, and swimming together. That changed in 1784, however, when York began his duties as William's body servant, a privileged position for a slave. York was strong, capable, and smart, which made him ideal for the job. When the Clark family moved to a new home in Kentucky that year, York made the trip with them. When John Clark died in 1799, York officially became William's property. At some point, York was allowed to marry a slave woman from a neighboring plantation. She had to remain with her master, however, and York stayed with Clark.

In 1803, William Clark received an invitation from his friend Meriwether Lewis to join him on an expedition to determine whether the Pacific Ocean could be reached by a water route across the continent. Though he could have left him behind on the plantation, Clark obviously valued York enough to want to include him in the adventure. York, as a slave, had no choice but to do as his master wished. Taking York along turned out to be a very good decision.

Though it would have been easy for the white men on the expedition, the Corps of Discovery, to let York do all the dirty work, it appears that they treated him more fairly. Perhaps it was because they were not used to owning slaves. He had an equal vote in the group.

There are many books that tell about the three years that Lewis and Clark and the Corps of Discovery spent exploring the lands beyond the western boundaries of the United States at that time. Most mention the valuable contributions that York was able to make to the expedition. His strength was needed to help handle the twenty-three thousand pounds of goods the Corps took with them, as well as to pull or push the keelboats along the rivers. York was an able hunter and was able to find other sources of food, such as watercress.

Probably the greatest contribution York made was something he had no control over. For many of the native tribes the Corps would meet along its way, black was a sacred color. Brave and successful warriors were allowed to paint their faces black. When they saw a man who was entirely black, and whose color did not wash off, they were amazed. They referred to him as "Big Medicine," meaning they thought he had special spiritual power. Near the end of a freezing winter, York was even able to use the respect the Indians had for him to get food from them after all other attempts had failed. His success ensured the survival of the Corps.

When the Lewis and Clark party finally returned to St. Louis on September 23, 1806, York briefly got to share in the glory. He was allowed to tell his part of the story to those who wanted to listen. Too soon he had to return to his position as Clark's personal servant. He did not share in any of the rewards given to the other members of the group. Though he did get to see his wife after his return, York soon had to leave her to accompany Clark to his new post as Indian agent for the West in St. Louis. This was to bring an end to the close relationship York and Clark had. York had wanted to stay close to his wife. Clark and York's bond was never the same. Sometime around 1816, Clark finally freed York. We know that York had difficulty living as a free black man. For one who did so much for our country, he died without anyone even noting his passing or his contributions to the opening of the West.

Nonfiction Reading Comprehension • 5-6 © 2005 Creative Teaching Press

Name _____ Date _____

Caches and Pirogues

bezoar	sawyer	gauntlet	cache	tippet	pirogue
cordelle	blunderbuss	sniggle	pemmican	clamons	weirs

Unscramble the words from the Lewis and Clark Voyage of Discovery. Use the words from the box for help.

1 Soldiers who needed to be punished were forced to run the **talugent.**

_____

2 Lewis received a **pettip** of ermine skins to wear around this shoulders.

_____

3 Wooden fences called **swire** were used to trap fish.

_____

4 A **obearz,** or hair ball, was sent back to Thomas Jefferson.

_____

5 A **yeraws** was a dead tree in the water that made travel dangerous.

_____

6 A **subrednblus** was shot off when they arrived back in St. Charles.

_____

7 The **gripeuo** had a flat bottom and a rudder and sometimes used a sail.

_____

8 Whatever they could not carry was stored in a **hecca** to be picked up on the way back.

_____

9 The **ecrolled** was used to pull the keelboat upstream.

_____

10 A **gligens** was a lure made of horsehair, which was used for fishing.

_____

11 To protect themselves in battle, Indians wore **smolanc** made from elk skin.

_____

12 Cakes of **cammpine** were made from buffalo, berries, and fat and eaten on the trail.

_____

Nonfiction Reading Comprehension • 5–6 © 2005 Creative Teaching Press

Name _____ Date _____

Say It Again

Rewrite each fact about York and the Lewis and Clark expedition. State the information more clearly.

1 The Corps of Discovery, including York, set up camp the first winter close to the Mississippi River across from the mouth of the Missouri River.

_____

_____

2 Three members of the Corps of Discovery were flogged for staying out all night dancing even though no one had said they could. It happened in May of 1804. York watched the punishment.

_____

_____

3 The only man to die on the expedition was Sergeant Charles Floyd, who probably had appendicitis since he was having stomach pains. York nursed Charles Floyd up until the time he died.

_____

_____

4 The Corps of Discovery spent the winter of 1804 in the Mandan villages, which are in present-day North Dakota. York assisted the others in building cabins to live in there that had beds to sleep in and benches and tables to eat at.

_____

_____

5 York's skin froze during a buffalo hunt in subzero weather.

_____

_____

6 In March of 1805, York was allowed to send a gift of a buffalo robe with pictures painted on it to his wife.

_____

_____

7 The Lewis and Clark expedition, along with York, reached the Pacific Ocean on November 7, 1805. It had taken a very difficult year and a half to get there.

_____

_____

Nonfiction Reading Comprehension • 5–6 © 2005 Creative Teaching Press

Clark's Main Man

Use details from the passage to support each main idea.

1 A slave's life was difficult for many reasons.

_____

_____

_____

_____

2 York was a valuable member of the Corps of Discovery.

_____

_____

_____

_____

3 Clark cared about York.

_____

_____

_____

_____

4 Some of the happiest times in York's life were probably when he was on the expedition.

_____

_____

_____

_____

Nonfiction Reading Comprehension • 5–6 © 2005 Creative Teaching Press

Name _____ Date _____

Artifacts

Match each picture with its description. Write the name of the artifact on the line.

   a. branding iron—a piece of iron that said "U.S. Capt. M. Lewis," which was used to mark trees wherever they went
   b. bull boat—a round boat made out of willow branches and buffalo skins
   c. espontoon—a weapon consisting of a 6-foot pole with a long, double-edged blade
   d. Hadley's quadrant—an instrument used for measuring distances
   e. keelboat—a long boat that could be sailed, rowed, pushed, or pulled along

1 _____

2 _____

3 _____

4 _____

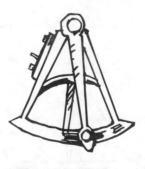

5 _____

Nonfiction Reading Comprehension • 5–6 © 2005 Creative Teaching Press

Five Points Long Ago

Five Points was an area of New York City known as a frightening and dangerous slum. It was named Five Points because the intersection of what are now Park, Worth, and Baxter Streets made five corners. All manner of criminals made their homes in this area, but there were also many hardworking immigrants who settled in the neighborhood after arriving in the United States. Five Points was so well-known that even Abraham Lincoln came to see it.

One section came to be known as Murderer's Alley. It was along one wall of the Old Brewery on Cross Street near Anthony and Orange Streets. The Old Brewery, originally called Coulter's, became a rooming house around 1838. It was not your typical rooming house, however. It was five stories tall. The main floor housed about seventy-five men and women and was nicknamed "The Den of Thieves." There were over 70 rooms upstairs where an additional 1,000 men, women, and children lived. Can you imagine living with so many other people? It was not a pleasant place to stay. There was at least one murder almost every night in the Old Brewery for over 15 years. Even the police did not want to go in there unless they were in a large group.

Unfortunately, the Five Points had problems from the beginning. The neighborhood itself was built on what had once been a beautiful lake. Around 1802, pollution from animal slaughter-houses, leather tanneries, and breweries had so fouled the water that the Collect Pond, as it was called, was drained and filled in to get rid of the awful smell and health problems associated with the pollution. It was on this landfill in 1813 that Five Points was built.

Most of the early residents were business-people who had their shops and their homes in the same building. Many made goods such as clothes or shoes. There were a few industries, such as Coulter's Brewery and factories to make glue and turpentine.

With the growth of the Industrial Revolution and immigration, however, Five Points began to change for the worse. Factories now made many of the same items the businesspeople had, only faster and cheaper. Children who had once been apprentices, learning the trade from these business people, now roamed the streets.

As businesses left the area, immigrants—primarily German and Irish—moved in. What had once been nice homes situated above the businesses were divided into many small, often windowless apartments. These became known as tenements. Many of these immigrants, fleeing famine or poverty in their own countries, arrived with nothing and had to take whatever housing they could find. Single people slept as many as twenty to a room in boardinghouses. Whole families crowded into an eight-by-ten room in tenements such as Misery Row. Just to be able to afford to live in these horrible conditions every-one in the family had to work very hard, including the children, who did everything from sweeping streets to shining shoes.

Because buildings had been built on the landfill, the land in Five Points was unstable. Buildings sank and streets flooded. Additionally, there were few connections to sewers, so it was difficult to dispose of the large amount of human waste. This, combined with the manure from the horses used for transportation and waste from the factories, made the environment very unhealthy.

Between 1850 and 1860, seven out of ten children under the age of two died each year. Many died from drinking the milk of diseased cows. Poor nutrition took its toll as well. Cholera from contaminated water and food and typhus transported by fleas from rats and mice created epidemics. Living in close quarters also contributed to the spread of diseases such as tuberculosis, small pox, and measles. The entire area finally had to be demolished in 1894.

Nonfiction Reading Comprehension • 5–6 © 2005 Creative Teaching Press

Slang Words

The less upstanding citizens of the Five Points had a language all their own. Here is some of the **cant,** or slang, that these criminals used, according to the New York City police chief at the time, George Matsell.

barking irons	crib	idea pot	polisher
grassville	roughs	sand	gapeseed
Richardsnary	goaways	city college	patter
wooden coat	crusher	squeal	stepping ken

Look at the words in the box. Fill in the blanks below with the slang word that matches each meaning.

1. the country __ __ __ __ __ __ __ __ __

2. house __ __ __ __

3. men who like to fight __ __ __ __ __ __

4. to tell on someone __ __ __ __ __ __

5. coffin __ __ __ __ __ __   __ __ __ __

6. talk __ __ __ __ __ __

7. head __ __ __ __   __ __ __

8. pistols __ __ __ __ __ __ __   __ __ __ __ __

9. trains __ __ __ __ __ __ __

10. spellbinding stories __ __ __ __ __ __ __ __

11. police officer __ __ __ __ __ __ __

12. a place to go dancing __ __ __ __ __ __ __ __   __ __ __ __

13. dictionary __ __ __ __ __ __ __ __ __ __ __

14. male prisoner __ __ __ __ __ __ __ __

15. guts, nerve __ __ __ __

16. jail __ __ __ __   __ __ __ __ __ __ __

Nonfiction Reading Comprehension • 5–6 © 2005 Creative Teaching Press

Name _____ Date _____

Which Came First?

For each pair of events, circle the letter of the one that came first.

1   a. The Old Brewery became a rooming house.
         b. People enjoyed visiting the Collect Pond.

2   a. Abraham Lincoln came to visit Five Points.
         b. The Collect Pond became too polluted.

3   a. Five Points was built.
         b. Immigrants escaping the Irish Potato Famine arrived in New York.

4   a. Seven out of ten children under the age of two died each year.
         b. The Old Brewery became a rooming house.

5   a. Craftsmen taught apprentices their trade.
         b. Buildings were divided up into apartments known as tenements.

6   a. The Collect Pond became too polluted.
         b. The Industrial Revolution allowed goods to be made faster and cheaper.

7   a. Five Points began to sink.
         b. Coulter's Brewery was a successful business.

8   a. Five points was torn down.
         b. People enjoyed visiting the Collect Pond.

Nonfiction Reading Comprehension • 5–6 © 2005 Creative Teaching Press

Name _____ Date _____

Why Was It So Miserable?

Fill in the missing causes and effects to complete the chart.

Cause	Effect
1	The police did not want to go into the Old Brewery unless they were in a large group.
2 The Collect Pond became too polluted.	
3 The Industrial Revolution allowed goods to be made faster and cheaper.	
4	Five Points began to sink and to flood.
5	German and Irish immigrants moved into Five Points.
6 There were few connections to sewers.	
7 Children drank milk from diseased cows.	
8	People got sick from cholera.
9	People got sick from typhus.
10	People caught tuberculosis, small pox, and measles.

Nonfiction Reading Comprehension • 5–6 © 2005 Creative Teaching Press

Growing Cotton

Growing cotton was hard work in the early days of American history. Days began at sunup and ended at dark with only a two-hour lunch break. Work in the cotton fields usually began in February or March. First, the debris from the previous year's crop had to be removed. Large stalks had to be pulled out by hand. Stalks under 4 feet tall could sometimes be mashed down with sticks. Harrows with metal teeth were used to remove debris and made the soil smooth and level. Plows and shovels were used to dig furrows, which were then fertilized, usually with manure. This was necessary because growing cotton severely depleted the soil.

In April, after the danger of frost had passed, farmers planted the cotton seed. This had to be done by hand. By May, it was time to thin the seedlings and remove the weeds. Time after time, a triangular cultivator blade called a sweep went between the rows, cutting off weeds below the surface of the soil. Then, each row had to be hoed by hand over and over again to keep the weeds away. By mid-June, the plants had grown to 6 to 12 inches. They were ready to bloom. About six weeks later, the cotton bolls would open, showing the fluffy, white cotton inside, and picking began around the second or third week in August. Again, all of the cotton had to be picked by hand.

The work to be done by hand was not over once the cotton was harvested. There was a variety of cotton called long-staple, and its seeds could be removed using a machine with rollers that was originally invented in India. This kind of cotton, however, could only be grown on the sea islands of South Carolina and in parts of Georgia. The other type of cotton—short-staple—was full of lots of sticky seeds. These all had to be removed manually, taking a single person almost a full day to clean 1 pound of cotton, and it was hard work. Most farmers couldn't make money selling cotton and primarily grew it for personal use. Even that was limited as it took twelve to fourteen days to produce 1 pound of cotton thread but only one to two days for wool thread or two to five days for flax thread. Cotton fabric was much easier to keep clean but much harder to make. Only 187,600 pounds of cotton were harvested in the entire U.S. in 1793. Once the cotton gin was invented that same year, it took care of the seed removal problem and the cotton-growing industry took off.

The expanding cotton industry ended up shaping American history. Slavery had been on its way out before the invention of the cotton gin. The need for slaves had decreased as farmers changed from growing tobacco to grain crops, which needed fewer people to help grow and harvest them. Also, after fighting for their own freedom in the American Revolution, there was a feeling among some people that they should not own slaves.

The cotton gin changed that. Suddenly, growing cotton became very profitable. The gin allowed a person to clean 50 pounds of cotton a day instead of 1 pound. With the invention of mechanical spinning machines, England's textile industry was willing to buy all the cotton that could be produced. In ten years, the amount of cotton produced increased to 93 million pounds. Growing and picking cotton still needed to be done by hand, however, which meant more people were needed. The number of slaves grew from about 657,000 to almost 1.3 million.

The South cannot be blamed completely for the continuation of slavery. Cotton was good for the entire country. Textile factories in the North made money spinning the cotton into cloth. With most of the South planted in cotton, food had to be purchased from Midwestern farmers. As Senator James Henry Hammond said in 1858, "What would happen if no cotton was furnished for three years? England would topple headlong and carry the whole civilized world with her. Cotton is King!"

Name _____ Date _____

Terms to Know

| bolls | continuation | cultivator | debris | expanding | fertilize |
| furrows | manually | mechanical | profitable | seedlings | textile |

Match each word from the box with its definition.

1 able to make money from _____

2 a tool used for loosening the soil _____

3 the trenches made by plowing the earth _____

4 to do by hand _____

5 trash _____

6 something that goes on in time _____

7 increasing in size _____

8 cloth _____

9 to make better able to grow things _____

10 having to do with machines _____

11 the pods of a plant _____

12 young plants _____

Nonfiction Reading Comprehension • 5–6 © 2005 Creative Teaching Press

How-to Book

Imagine you are writing a book that explains how to grow cotton. What information would you need to include? Circle the topics that you would include in your book. Cross out the topics that would not belong.

1 insects that can harm crops

2 the history of cotton in India

3 weather during harvest

4 preparing the soil

5 how cotton is spun into thread

6 how much seed to buy

7 buying a tractor

8 kinds of cotton

9 tools for planting, maintaining, and harvesting

10 how cotton is dyed

11 how to harvest

12 the textile industry in England

13 when to thin the seedlings

14 how to paint your barn

15 storing the harvest

Name _____ Date _____

A Letter to Cousin Jeb

Dear Cousin,

   I recently moved to Texas and want to start growing cotton here. Since you have such a successful plantation in Mississippi, I was hoping you could give me some advice on how to get started.

Sincerely,

Jeb

Use the information from the passage to write a letter to Cousin Jeb giving him advice.

Dear Jeb,

   If you want to grow cotton successfully, the first thing you should do is _____

_____

_____

_____

_____

_____

_____

_____

_____

_____

_____

_____

_____

_____

_____

_____

_____

_____

Nonfiction Reading Comprehension • 5–6 © 2005 Creative Teaching Press

Dr. Mary Walker

The Civil War in the United States of America was the worst war in our history. More than 618,000 Americans died. Many people are not aware, however, of how many women were involved in the Civil War. Thousands of women served as nurses. Others provided provisions to soldiers in the field or sold supplies to those who were fighting. Most women kept the family farms or businesses running while the men went off to fight. It is believed that some 400 women actually served for the Union or for the Confederacy in the Civil War as soldiers or as spies, and more than 80 of them were either killed or wounded in the various battles.

Among these women, one stands out. She was the first and only woman to receive the Congressional Medal of Honor. She was proud of this medal and wore it every day until she died at the age of eighty-six.

Mary Edwards Walker grew up in Oswego, New York, the daughter of a country doctor. At the age of twenty-one, she became only the second woman in the United States to receive a medical degree, receiving her degree from Syracuse Medical College. She briefly practiced medicine in Columbus, Ohio. In 1856, she married Albert Miller, whom she met in college, but she never took his last name during their thirteen years of marriage. They began a medical practice in Rome, New York. In 1862, she received an additional degree from Hygeia Therapeutic College in New York.

At the outbreak of the Civil War, Mary went to work for the Union Army, enlisting in Louisville, Kentucky. Because the army would not hire female doctors, she worked as a nurse. She began at the First Battle of Manassas (Bull Run) on July 21, 1861. In October of 1861, she went to the Patent Office Hospital in Washington, D.C. Later, in September of 1863, she served as a "volunteer surgeon" in an army hospital in Chattanooga, Tennessee, following the Battle of Chickamauga. Eventually, she was appointed as surgeon to the 52nd Ohio Infantry Regiment under the command of Colonel Dan McCook.

Mary did not just help the Union soldiers. She often crossed enemy lines to aid women and children in the area. On one such mission on April 10, 1864, she ran into a group of Confederate soldiers. Unfortunately, she was wearing her Union uniform at the time, so they arrested her and sent her to prison in Richmond, Virginia. She was released on August 12, 1864, in a prisoner exchange. She was pleased that she was considered an equal trade for a Confederate officer.

By September, when the battle of Atlanta was fought, she was in Louisville, Kentucky, once again serving as a surgeon. She never returned to the front lines. Instead, she practiced medicine in Louisville at a female prison and at a shelter for orphans in Tennessee for the duration of the Civil War. She was proud of her service to her country. She wanted people to know that women in uniform also fought for their freedom.

In January of 1866, Mary Walker received the Congressional Medal of Honor, the nation's highest award for valor. It was the only citation she was eligible for since, as a woman, she was not allowed to be a commissioned officer and could only receive recognition as a civilian. She had been recommended for the award by both General George Thomas and General William T. Sherman. In 1917, an attempt was made to take away her medal, saying she may not have deserved it. She refused to return it. Her right to the Medal of Honor was confirmed by President Jimmy Carter on June 10, 1977. The medal is now displayed in the Pentagon. The United States Postal Service issued a twenty-cent stamp in her honor in 1982. In 2000, Dr. Mary Edwards Walker was inducted into the Women's Hall of Fame.

Nonfiction Reading Comprehension • 5–6 © 2005 Creative Teaching Press

Name _____ Date _____

Civil War Medicine

ague	apoplexy	bilious fever	lumbago
cramp colic	diphtheria	dresser	paroxysm
milk sickness	gripe	chilblain	consumption
St. Vitus dance	palsy	dropsy	lung fever

Use the words from the box to complete the crossword puzzle.

Across
1. Congestive heart failure
2. Convulsion
3. Loss of muscle control or paralysis
9. Pain in fingers and toes caused by exposure to extreme cold
10. Fever and chills from malaria
11. Surgeon's assistant in a hospital
12. Disease from the milk from cattle that had eaten poisonous weeds
13. Stroke; leads to softening of the brain
15. Appendicitis

Down
1. Contagious disease of the throat
4. Backache
5. Tuberculosis
6. Fever caused by liver problems
7. Pneumonia
8. Nervous twitching
14. Flu

Nonfiction Reading Comprehension • 5–6 © 2005 Creative Teaching Press

Name _____ Date _____

An Interview with the Doctor

Imagine that you have interviewed Dr. Mary Edwards Walker. Write each question above the answer she might have given to it.

- Why do you think your medical practices were not successful?
- How did you feel when they tried to take away your Medal of Honor?
- After the Civil War, you worked to get women the right to vote. Why did you think this was important?
- What were your views on women's clothing?

 1 _____

_____

I was a fan of Amelia Bloomer and agreed with her that women's clothes were unhealthy and restricted movement. The uniform I wore during the Civil War was a short skirt over long, loose trousers. When I was older, I liked wearing men's clothing, complete with a top hat! Others didn't like me dressing this way, and I was even arrested for it!

 2 _____

_____

Women did not have very many rights. People needed to know that the thoughts and opinions of men and women are equally important. Women did so much during the war, but we were still treated like second-class citizens. I was smart enough to be a doctor, but they thought I wasn't intelligent enough to vote.

 3 _____

_____

I think people were just not ready to accept a woman doctor. I was only the second woman in the entire United States to graduate from medical school. The first was Elizabeth Blackwell, and she was originally let into medical school as a joke.

4 _____

_____

I was very angry. I refused to return it. I enjoyed wearing it and was very proud that I was the only woman to receive this honor.

Nonfiction Reading Comprehension • 5–6 © 2005 Creative Teaching Press

Presenting to the Class

Imagine that you are going to give a presentation to the class about Dr. Mary Edwards Walker. Use note cards to help you remember the important details about her life that you want to talk about. Each point should be short but informative.

Using the passage, fill in the note cards below with points you want to cover for each subject.

Early Life

• born in Oswego, New York

Civil War Service

Awards and Recognition

Nonfiction Reading Comprehension • 5–6 © 2005 Creative Teaching Press

The Gettysburg Address

The Battle of Gettysburg was fought on the first three days of July in 1863 on fields in south-central Pennsylvania. The Confederate troops were led by Robert E. Lee. He made a desperate, full-out, frontal assault on the Union forces. Their attempts to push further north were repelled by General George Meade. It was to be a turning point in the three-year-old Civil War. The Confederates were forced to retreat southward, and the rest of the war would be spent defending Southern territory.

When the battle was over, Andrew Curtin, the governor of Pennsylvania, asked David Wills, a Gettysburg-area judge, to oversee the cleanup efforts. The fighting had left thousands of dead soldiers and hundreds of dead horses strewn across the fields, and the bodies were beginning to bloat in the July sun. Wills contacted the eighteen states who had had citizens killed in the fighting and they agreed to the creation of a national cemetery. Seventeen acres of land were purchased and an architect, William Saunders, began to draw up the plans. Soon, the work of burying the dead was able to begin, though, at the time of the cemetery dedication, less than half of the dead would have been removed from the field graves for reburial.

The dedication of the cemetery was scheduled for October 23, and at the end of September, Wills invited a famous orator of the time, Edward Everett, to give a speech. Everett needed more time, so the date for the ceremony was changed to November 19. On November 2, Wills wrote a letter to President Abraham Lincoln, inviting him to participate in the ceremonies, which he thought would "doubtless be very imposing and solemnly impressive."

The day of the dedication was sunny and the air was crisp. Abraham Lincoln arrived at the cemetery on horseback in the midst of a procession. He had spent the earlier part of the day greeting local citizens at the home of David Wills. The ceremonies began. Everett stood on the rough, wooden stage built for the event and gave a

two-hour speech, which was greatly praised by the newpapers the next day. When it was Lincoln's turn, he stood at the podium, removed his speech from his pocket and began to read. Lincoln delivered his Gettysburg Address in about two minutes, and there was no applause when he finished. In fact, some people did not even realize he had spoken. Its contents were barely even mentioned in the press. After he went back to his seat, Lincoln said, "That speech won't scour. It is a flat failure." Everett, however, wrote a note to Lincoln the next day, acknowledging the power of Lincoln's words. "I should be glad if I could flatter myself that I came as near to the central idea of the occasion in two hours as you did in two minutes," he wrote.

There are many stories about when and how the Gettysburg Address was written. It doesn't really matter. The speech Lincoln gave that day has become one of the greatest pieces of writing in American history. It is as much a poem as anything else. In only 272 words, he summed up the reasons why the United States existed and why it was so important to preserve the Union. He managed to express the many different emotions that Americans were feeling. There are those who will argue that the Gettysburg Address was nothing more than propaganda on Lincoln's part, an attempt to raise morale for a war that was not always popular. Time has proven the power of his words, however. We remain one united country, with a "government of the people by the people for the people."

Nonfiction Reading Comprehension • 5–6 © 2005 Creative Teaching Press

Name _____   Date _____

Lincoln's Words

conceived	consecrate	dedicated	detract	devotion	endure
engaged	full measure	hallow	honored	in vain	liberty
perish	proposition	propriety	resolve	score	task

Match each word from the box with its definition.

1 twenty years ___ ___ ___ ___ ___

2 created or thought of ___ ___ ___ ___ ___ ___ ___ ___ ___

3 freedom ___ ___ ___ ___ ___ ___ ___

4 set apart for or committed to ___ ___ ___ ___ ___ ___ ___ ___ ___

5 belief or idea ___ ___ ___ ___ ___ ___ ___ ___

6 in the middle of doing; involved ___ ___ ___ ___ ___ ___ ___

7 continue or last ___ ___ ___ ___ ___ ___

8 being proper, polite, or acceptable ___ ___ ___ ___ ___ ___ ___ ___ ___

9 devote or dedicate ___ ___ ___ ___ ___ ___ ___ ___ ___

10 make holy ___ ___ ___ ___ ___ ___

11 take attention away from ___ ___ ___ ___ ___ ___

12 job or chore ___ ___ ___ ___

13 respected ___ ___ ___ ___ ___ ___ ___

14 loyalty or faithfulness ___ ___ ___ ___ ___ ___ ___ ___

15 total or complete ___ ___ ___ ___ ___ ___ ___ ___ ___ ___ ___

16 promise ___ ___ ___ ___ ___ ___ ___

17 for nothing ___ ___ ___ ___ ___ ___

18 die ___ ___ ___ ___ ___ ___

Name _____ Date _____

But What Did It Mean?

Rewrite the Gettysburg Address in your own words. Use the vocabulary page, "Lincoln's Words," and a dictionary to help you.

Four score and seven years ago our fathers brought forth on this continent a new nation, conceived in liberty and dedicated to the proposition that all men are created equal.

Now we are engaged in a great civil war, testing whether that nation or any nation so conceived and so dedicated can long endure. We are met on a great battlefield of that war. We have come to dedicate a portion of that field as a final resting-place for those who here gave their lives that that nation might live. It is altogether fitting and proper that we should do this.

But in a larger sense, we cannot dedicate, we cannot consecrate, we cannot hallow this ground. The brave men, living and dead who struggled here have consecrated it far above our poor power to add or detract. The world will little note nor long remember what we say here, but it can never forget what they did here. It is for us the living rather to be dedicated here to the unfinished work which they who fought here have thus far so nobly advanced. It is rather for us to be here dedicated to the great task remaining before us—that from these honored dead we take increased devotion to that cause for which they gave the last full measure of devotion—that we here highly resolve that these dead shall not have died in vain, that this nation under God shall have a new birth of freedom, and that government of the people, by the people, for the people shall not perish from the earth.

_____

_____

_____

_____

_____

_____

_____

_____

_____

_____

Name _____ Date _____

Writing Home

Imagine that you were in Gettysburg at the cemetery dedication on November 19, 1863. Use the passage, reference books, and your imagination to fill in the graphic organizer.

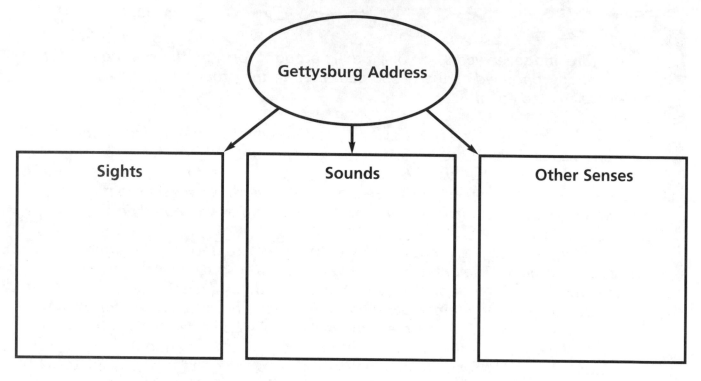

Now imagine that you are writing a letter to your mother who was not able to be at the dedication. Use information from the graphic organizer to write your letter. Include lots of sensory images so she can understand what it was like to be there.

November 19, 1863

Dear Mother,

    Today I was at the dedication of the national cemetery at Gettysburg, Pennsylvania.

_____

_____

_____

_____

_____

_____

_____

_____

                                Love,

Name _____ Date _____

Lincoln's Ideals

Read each statement. Based on the Gettysburg Address, write **agree** if you think Abraham Lincoln would have agreed with the statement. Write **disagree** if you think that he would have disagreed with it.

1 _____ The Founding Fathers were great men.

2 _____ All men should have equal rights.

3 _____ The Founding Fathers didn't really think the United States would last.

4 _____ It is sometimes necessary for people to die to preserve freedom.

5 _____ Southerners should be allowed to do whatever they want.

6 _____ People should be allowed to have slaves.

7 _____ People should be very respectful when visiting the cemetery.

8 _____ The United States was founded so that people could be successful and make money.

9 _____ If the remaining soldiers didn't go fight, the ones who died would have died for no reason.

10 _____ Lincoln was going to be the greatest president ever.

11 _____ If the Union didn't win the war, that would be fine.

12 _____ People should vote.

13 _____ The Gettysburg Address was going to be famous.

14 _____ The Union needed to win the war.

15 _____ The Battle of Gettysburg would never be forgotten.

Krakatau

Krakatau, sometimes spelled Krakatoa, was an island in the Indian Ocean near the islands of Sumatra and Java. No one lived on the island, but it was visited occasionally by natives who would pick fruit there. Sailors traveling the seas in the area during the 1800s knew it had once been a volcano, but they believed it was extinct. Krakatau was to prove them wrong in a big way.

The first hints that Krakatau was still active occurred in the spring of 1883, when a few rumbling earthquakes began. Rather than being frightened, people found the possible eruption interesting. Some packed a picnic and took a boat to have a look. When they climbed up the volcano, they saw steam rising from a 90-foot opening, but they were still not alarmed.

By summer, the volcano had gotten quite noisy and could be heard for miles and miles. It began spitting dust into the air, which darkened the sky around it. People began to get very uneasy in anticipation of an eruption.

The skies around the Sunda Strait between Java and Sumatra were almost completely black with dust by the evening of Sunday, August 26, 1883. Against the dark backdrop of the sky, one could see the glow from the top of Krakatua. One hundred miles away in the Indonesian capital of Jakarta, windows rattled as the earth trembled.

The next morning at around 5:30 a.m. the eruptions began. There were a few minor explosions before ten o'clock. Then, in one gigantic blast, two-thirds of the island disappeared. The explosion was so great that it was heard 3,000 miles away.

The destruction was not over, however. The collapse of the island into the now empty magma chamber below sea level led to pyroclastic flows and tsunamis, destroying 165 villages along the coasts of neighboring islands. Over 36,000 people died. Pyroclastic flows are the deadliest element of a volcanic eruption. They are made up of ash and rock and flow outward from the eruption at hundreds of miles an hour at temperatures of 300 to 1,300 degrees. The tidal waves caused by the cataclysm reached heights of 40 feet. Boats on the coast were thrown as much as 28 miles inland. One island, Sebesi, was completely submerged, wiping away all traces of its 3,000 inhabitants. The firsthand accounts of the huge waves with hot, glowing lava floating on their surfaces are terrifying.

The explosion of Krakatau affected the entire globe. Barometers all over the world measured the pressure waves radiating outward from the explosion. The waves continued to bounce back and forth for five days. The effects of the sea waves were measured in Yemen twelve hours after the eruption. They had traveled a distance "usually traversed by a good steamer in 12 days." Ash in the stratosphere caused the sun to look blue or green. This ash was to influence the globe for years to come as it engulfed the planet. It caused such red sunsets as far away as New York that people feared the city was on fire. It was three years before unusual sunsets subsided. It took even longer for the climate to return to normal. The ash filtered out the sun's rays and lowered the temperature of the earth. Normal temperatures did not resume until 1888.

In December of 1927, an island called the Child of Krakatau began to appear above the surface of the ocean, the result of the volcanic activity in the area that continues to this day. It now rises over 600 feet into the air. It is unlikely that an explosion like the one in 1883 will ever happen again at this site, but the Child of Krakatau serves as a reminder that the earth below us is very active and often unpredictable.

Nonfiction Reading Comprehension • 5–6 © 2005 Creative Teaching Press

Name _____   Date _____

Taking a "Krak" at Vocabulary

anticipation	cataclysm	collapse	engulfed	eruption
extinct	filtered	inhabitants	magma chamber	radiating
pyroclastic flow	stratosphere	submerged	subsided	tsunami
uneasy	unpredictable			

Use the words from the box to complete the crossword puzzle.

Across
3. nervous
4. underwater
9. tidal wave
10. feeling of excitement about something that is going to happen
11. cloud of ash and rock after a volcanic eruption
12. fall down
15. not certain what will happen

Down
1. people who live in a place
2. moving away from
4. layer of the atmosphere high above the earth
5. horrible, violent event
6. went away
7. took out
8. opening beneath the ground filled with melted rock
13. no longer alive
14. surrounded
16. bursting through

Dear Diary

Imagine that you are living near the island of Krakatau in 1883. Use the passage to help you describe what you might have seen, felt, or heard at that time to complete the diary pages.

May 20, 1883

Dear Diary,

_____
_____
_____
_____
_____
_____
_____
_____
_____
_____
_____
_____
_____

August 26, 1883

Dear Diary,

_____
_____
_____
_____
_____
_____
_____
_____
_____
_____
_____
_____
_____

August 27, 1883

Dear Diary,

_____
_____
_____
_____
_____
_____
_____
_____
_____
_____
_____

August 30, 1883

Dear Diary,

_____
_____
_____
_____
_____
_____
_____
_____
_____
_____
_____

Name _____ Date _____

And Then What Happened?

Fill in the missing causes and effects to complete the chart.

Cause	Effect
①	People realized that Krakatau was not extinct.
② Krakatau began spitting dust into the air.	
③	People began to worry that Krakatau was going to erupt.
④	Windows in Jakarta rattled.
⑤ The magma chamber emptied.	
⑥	Two-thirds of the island disappeared.
⑦ Pyroclastic flows moved outward from the explosion.	
⑧	People were swept away by the water.
⑨ Ash was blown high into the atmosphere.	
⑩	The Child of Krakatau appeared in December of 1927.

Nonfiction Reading Comprehension • 5–6 © 2005 Creative Teaching Press

Yellow Journalism

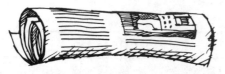

"Extra! Extra! Read all about it!" shouted the newsboy on the corner in 1898. It didn't matter if he was selling Joseph Pulitzer's New York *World* or William Randolph Hearst's New York *Morning Journal* or one of the other thirteen newspapers published in New York at the time. The headlines were sensational.

In 1898, there was no radio, movies, or television. People got their entertainment and their information from reading, especially newspapers. One-fourth of the adult population read at least one newspaper a week. The Industrial Revolution made it possible for papers to be printed faster and in greater numbers. In 1896, advances in technology allowed Pulitzer to add color comics to his paper, which appealed to readers. A popular comic character, the Yellow Kid, eventually lent its name to a kind of newspaper writing known as yellow journalism.

R. F. Outcault began drawing the Yellow Kid in the comic "Hogan's Alley" for the *World.* It was as popular as many cartoon characters are today. Collector cards are not a new idea; the Yellow Kid had them. After nine months, Outcault was lured away by Hearst and the Yellow Kid moved to the *Morning Journal.* It was part of the ongoing battle between Pulitzer and Hearst to dominate the New York newspaper market.

Usually competition makes the rivals produce a better product. In the case of Pulitzer and Hearst, however, their rivalry did not lead to better quality news publications. Instead, they sought to report bigger scandals and more outrageous stories. Headlines such as "One Mad Blow Kills Child" and "Real American Monsters and Dragons" showed up on the front pages. In some cases, the papers stole stories right from each other's pages. The *World* got caught stealing a fake story, printed in the *Journal* for just that pur-

pose. Pulitzer was very embarrassed. Hearst gloated.

As it often does, war gave the newspaper business a boost. The Spanish-American War in 1898 became the first war in which journalists played an important part. The successful laying of a trans-Atlantic telegraph cable in 1866 made communication faster than ever before. Journalists could transmit their stories to the United States in hours instead of weeks. Because so many people were reading the papers, what they printed had a strong effect on public opinion. When a rebellion against Spanish rule broke out in Cuba in 1895, journalists went to the Caribbean nation to cover the story. Some were welcomed; others were not. The stories were transmitted to New York. "Spanish Cannibalism" and "Amazon Warriors Fight For Rebels" screamed the headlines. There was often little truth about what was happening in Cuba in the articles printed in the *Journal* or the *World,* but people bought papers anyway. Based on what was in print, public opinion started to swing in favor of America helping the Cubans gain their freedom.

On the evening of February 15, 1898, the American battleship the *Maine* exploded near the coast of Havana, Cuba. It was what the "yellow papers" had been waiting for. We now know that the explosion was the result of a fire on board the ship, but at the time, the New York papers were sure the Spanish were behind it. They even printed drawings showing how the Spanish attached bombs to the ship. In the week after the disaster, as many as five million copies of the *World* were sold. At least eight pages a day in the *Journal* were devoted to news from Cuba. Americans were shouting, "Remember the Maine!" By April 25, fueled in part by demands in the press, the United States declared war on Spain.

Over time, journalists have become more responsible. There are still those who will print anything to make a buck, but readers who demand the truth create a market for the truth.

Nonfiction Reading Comprehension • 5–6 © 2005 Creative Teaching Press

Name _____ Date _____

Parts of a Newspaper

Use the words and definitions to label the newspaper illustration.

A. **byline**: name of the writer of the article

B. **caption or cutline**: words below a picture

C. **cut**: picture

D. **dateline**: date and or location of the story

E. **editorial**: a piece of writing that presents opinions rather than facts

F. **head or headline**: title of an article

G. **jumpline**: tells what page a story is continued on

H. **photo credit**: name of the photographer who took the picture

Name _____ Date _____

Five Ws and an H

Think of a recent exciting event that happened at your school and list details about it.

What happened? _____

Who was involved? _____

When did it happen? _____

Where did it happen? _____

Why did it happen? _____

How did it happen? _____

Other details: _____

Use the information you listed above to write a news story about the event.

1. Start with a lead. It is a single sentence that answers the questions *Who? What? When?* and *Where?*
2. Next answer the questions *Why?* and *How?* Always start with the most important or interesting information and work toward the least important details.
3. Remember that newspaper articles are written so that the readers can get the most important information in the first paragraph. They only need to read to the end if they are interested in knowing more.

_____

_____

_____

_____

_____

_____

_____

_____

_____

_____

_____

_____

_____

_____

Nonfiction Reading Comprehension • 5–6 © 2005 Creative Teaching Press

Name _____ Date _____

Headlines

Match each fact with the sensational headline a yellow journalist might give it.

1 ____ A thundershower is predicted.

2 ____ Squirrels are stealing from birdfeeders.

3 ____ The beach is closed due to high bacteria levels.

4 ____ A doctor puts a man on a diet.

5 ____ The Boy Scouts go camping.

6 ____ The Venus flytrap traps insects.

7 ____ Grandma got a new flyswatter.

8 ____ A pet snake got out of its cage.

9 ____ A brother and sister have to clean their rooms.

10 ____ A brand-new baseball player hits the ball.

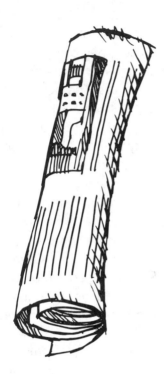

a. CHILDREN FORCED TO SLEEP WITHOUT BEDS!

b. **Pollution Could Cause Epidemic!**

c. **DEADLIEST YEAR EVER FOR FLIES!**

d. **Children Forced to Labor for No Pay!**

e. **Eight-Year-Old Has 1.000 Average!**

f. Storm of the Century to Strike!

g. Meat-Eating Plant Attacks!

h. MAN DENIED FOOD!

i. **PYTHON FOUND IN ATTIC!**

j. **Rodents Terrorize City!**

Axis Sally and Tokyo Rose

During World War II, American soldiers, known as GIs, were far from home, fighting in Europe and the Pacific. When they were not in battle, a popular pastime for some was listening to the radio. They could hear music from back home. In between were the voices of various women deejays. The best known of these women were Axis Sally and Tokyo Rose.

It is an interesting twist that a radio personality named Tokyo Rose never existed. It was just the nickname the GIs came up with for female broadcasters on Radio Tokyo (NHK). In truth, Orphan Ann was their favorite announcer, and in real life her name was Iva Ikuko Toguri.

Iva Toguri was born on the Fourth of July in 1916, in Los Angeles, California. She was a *Nisei,* or second-generation Japanese-American. She graduated from college at UCLA. She was hoping to become a doctor, but Toguri's aunt became ill in Japan, and she was sent to help care for her in 1941. Unfortunately, there were difficulties with the paperwork when she tried to return to the United States that November. One month later, with the bombing of Pearl Harbor, war was declared, and Toguri was trapped in Japan for the duration of the war.

Toguri worked hard to survive. Her relatives could not allow her to stay with them. Growing up in the U.S., she had not learned Japanese, but she had to now. Again and again, the *Kempeitai,* military police, asked her to give up her American citizenship. She refused.

Eventually, Toguri got a job as a typist for Radio Tokyo. There she became friends with prisoners of war, who were being forced to broadcast propaganda. When NHK wanted a woman's voice, they chose Toguri. She worked with them to sabotage her own broadcasts.

At the end of the war, Toguri made a mistake. The term Tokyo Rose was well-known by then. Reporters were eager to know who Rose was and were willing to pay for an interview. Toguri still needed to find a way to get back to the U.S., and she needed money. She said that she was Tokyo Rose. Instead of money and a ticket home, she was arrested and put in prison.

She finally returned to the United States in 1948. Unfortunately, it was for her trial for treason. She was only found guilty on one count—"That she did speak into a microphone concerning the loss of ships." She was given a $10,000 fine and sentenced to ten years in prison. After a reexamination of the facts, Toguri received a pardon from President Gerald Ford in 1977.

The woman the GIs called Axis Sally was really named Mildred Elizabeth Sisk Gillars. She was born in Portland, Maine, on November 29, 1900. She moved around a lot as a child, eventually ending up in Ohio. She attended Ohio Wesleyan University and majored in drama but could not meet the requirements for graduation. (She finally did complete her degree in 1973.)

Gillars did everything she could to become an actress but was never really successful. In 1935, she moved to Germany and began teaching English. The pay was not good, however, and she took a job with Radio Berlin and swoar an oath of loyalty to Germany. Max Otto Koischewitz, one of her former teachers, was the program director there. From December 11, 1941, until May 6, 1945, she broadcast her program, "Home Sweet Home," across Europe under his direction.

Gillars' broadcasts were very different from Toguri's. She taunted soldiers about what their sweethearts were doing while they were away. She posed as a Red Cross worker to interview wounded soldiers and then mixed propaganda with it for her broadcast. Her most famous broadcast occurred on May 11, 1944. It was a play called *Vision of Invasion* and was supposed to make the soldiers fear the upcoming D-Day invasion with its horrible battle sounds.

After the war, Gillars was also tried for treason. She was convicted on one count for the *Vision of Invasion* broadcast and received a $10,000 fine. She remained in prison until 1961. She became a private school teacher in Columbus, Ohio. She died on June 25, 1988.

Nonfiction Reading Comprehension • 5–6 © 2005 Creative Teaching Press

Name _____ Date _____

Kilroy Was Here

acronym	blitz	blockbuster	task force	jeep
dry run	genocide	gremlin	gung ho	walkie-talkie
kamikaze	radar	concentration camp		

Many new words had their origins in World War II. Match each word from the box with its definition.

1　imaginary creature that caused machines to break ___ ___ ___ ___ ___ ___ ___

2　sudden bombardment ___ ___ ___ ___ ___

3　suicide pilot who would crash into a ship ___ ___ ___ ___ ___ ___ ___ ___

4　place where people were imprisoned

___ ___ ___ ___ ___ ___ ___ ___ ___ ___ ___ ___ ___ ___ ___ ___ ___

5　word, like scuba, made up from the initials of a series of words

___ ___ ___ ___ ___ ___ ___

6　a general-purpose army vehicle ___ ___ ___ ___

7　a portable two-way radio ___ ___ ___ ___ ___ ___ -

___ ___ ___ ___ ___ ___

8　the deliberate destruction of an entire group of people

___ ___ ___ ___ ___ ___ ___ ___

9　enthusiastic ___ ___ ___ ___ - ___ ___

10　practice for an event ___ ___ ___ ___ ___ ___

11　device used for detecting ships and planes ___ ___ ___ ___ ___

12　very large or successful ___ ___ ___ ___ ___ ___ ___ ___ ___ ___ ___

13　group put together to meet a goal ___ ___ ___ ___ ___ ___ ___ ___ ___

Guilty or Not?

Choose either Mildred Gillars or Iva Toguri. Use information from the passage with reasons she should or should not have been convicted of treason.

Should Have Been Convicted	Should Not Have Been Convicted

Use the information to write a persuasive paragraph stating why you think she should or should not have been convicted of treason.

    Based on the reading, I think _____

should / should not have been convicted of treason. First of all, _____

_____

_____

_____

_____

_____

_____

_____

_____

_____

_____

Nonfiction Reading Comprehension • 5–6 © 2005 Creative Teaching Press

Commentators in Common

Write each statement in the correct place on the Venn diagram to compare Axis Sally and Tokyo Rose.

- forced to broadcast
- chose to broadcast
- nickname came from GIs
- American citizen
- was welcomed by enemy country
- was not welcomed by enemy country
- graduated from college before the war
- did not graduate from college before the war
- wanted to be an actress
- wanted to be a doctor
- born in Maine
- born in California
- convicted of treason
- fined $10,000

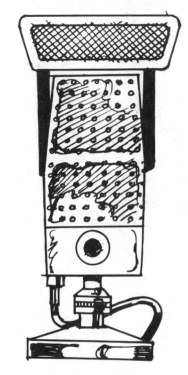

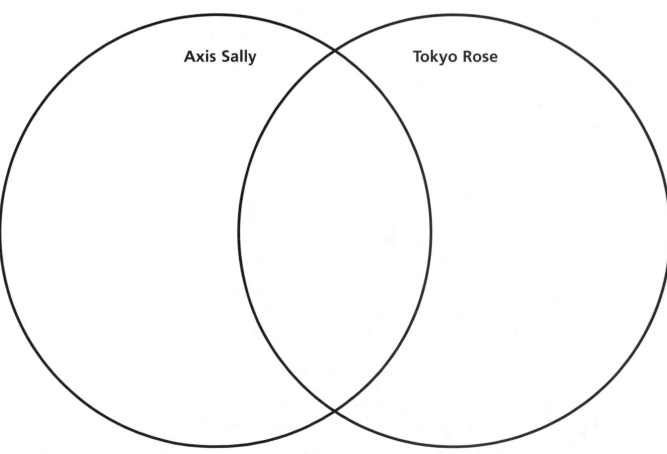

Axis Sally

Tokyo Rose

"Captain" Bill Pinkney

"Here I am, a descendent of slaves, making the Middle Passage not as cargo in the hull, but as Master of the Ship." These words were spoken by William Pinkney as he sailed the *Sortilege* along the historic route used by slave traders in the 1700 and 1800s. This voyage, which began in November of 1998 and took five months, traveled between Puerto Rico, Brazil, Ghana, Senegal, Cuba, and the United States, tracing the paths used by those who brought Africans to slavery in America. Pinkney made the trip in a 78-foot ketch, a type of sailboat, with three crew members and with various teams comprised of nine teachers, who created lessons while on board for students throughout the U.S. While this "journey of personal discovery" was important for Pinkney to connect with his African ancestors and for the crew to share their experiences with tens of thousands of children in 160 schools through the Internet, it was not the first important voyage for this accomplished sailor.

Bill Pinkney was born in Chicago on September 15, 1953. The Bronzeville area of the city where he lived gave him access to views of Lake Michigan. The sight of that big body of water combined with reading stories about the sea inspired him to join the navy after finishing high school. There he served as a hospital corpsman for eight years. Eventually, he ended up as a marketing representative for the Revlon cosmetics company, becoming an accomplished yachtsman along the way. In 1986, he became a U.S. Coast Guard certified Master on the Great Lakes. He received his ocean certification in 1990.

Being a grandfather inspired Pinkney's greatest achievement. He wanted to find a way to teach his grandchildren about the importance of education as well as the values of persistance, dedication, and duty. He wanted to show that children could make their dreams come true by taking the responsibility of doing everything it takes to make it happen.

The dream that Bill Pinkney chose to live out was that of circumnavigating, or sailing all the way around, the globe solo. It took him five years to get the financial backing for the trip. "Columbus, Magellan, me—we all wanted to go to sea, but had to get somebody else to pay for it. If you're not rich, you have to," said Pinkney.

He began his voyage in 1991, taking the southern and most dangerous route around the world. His journey took him around the five great capes—the Cape of Good Hope, Cape Horn, Cape Leeuwin, South East Cape, and Southwest Cape. Twenty-two months after he began, Pinkney sailed into Boston Harbor on June 9, 1992, aboard the 47-foot *Commitment*. He had become the first African American and the fourth American ever to complete the trip.

After these two incredible voyages, Bill Pinkney captained another ship until his retirement. A 129-foot replica of the slave ship *Amistad* was built by the state of Connecticut to commemorate the "Amistad Incident," in which slaves revolted in an attempt to gain their freedom. Eventually, they were granted that freedom by the Supreme Court. As Master of the ship, Bill Pinkney sailed the waters of the United States, sharing a message about human dignity and rights and about peace among the races. He continues to teach young people to follow their dreams and that nothing is impossible if they put their minds to it.

Nonfiction Reading Comprehension • 5–6 © 2005 Creative Teaching Press

Sailing Words

bow: forward part
crosstrees: crosspiece on mast
foremast: mast nearest the bow
jib: triangular sail from foremast to bow
keel: center bottom of the boat; keeps it upright
main boom: long beam across the bottom of the sail
main mast: sail second from the bow

main sail: biggest sail on the main mast
rudder: in the stern of the boat; used for steering
stem: bow of the ship
stern: rear of the boat
topmast: uppermost mast
topsail: sail attached to the topmast
transom: beams or planks that make up the stern

Use the words from the box to label the picture of a schooner. *Hint:* The schooner is sailing away from you.

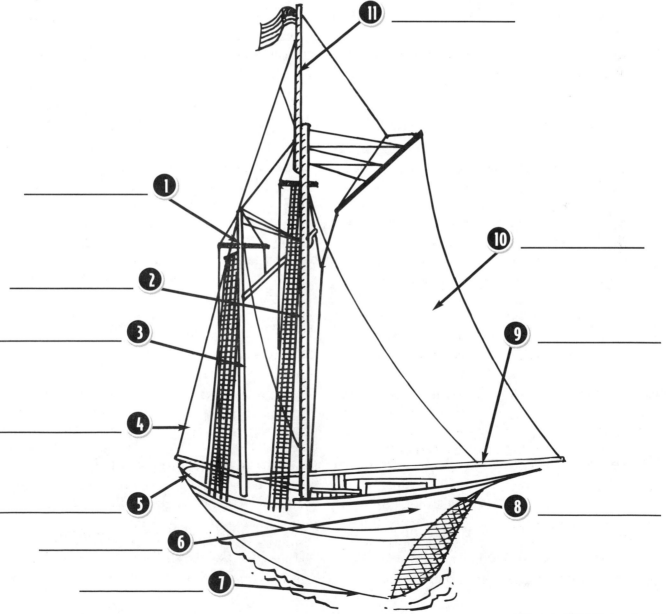

Character Builders

| caring | citizenship | dedication | fairness | loyalty |
| patience | perseverance | respect | responsibility | trustworthiness |

Bill Pinkney wanted to demonstrate important values to his grandchildren. Match each positive character trait from the box with its description.

1 Joel listens politely when someone is talking in class.

_____

2 Caitlin is having a hard time learning to play the piano, but she keeps practicing.

_____

3 Matthew helps pick up trash around the school.

_____

4 Ava stays friends with Li even when the other girls don't want to be her friend anymore.

_____

5 Jamie plays one game of tetherball on the playground, then lets others have a turn.

_____

6 Luis knows that if he wants to become a better reader he needs to read every day.

_____

7 Kristin doesn't get upset when her little sister colors on her schoolwork.

_____

8 Morgan helps a new student fit in at school.

_____

9 Leo finds a wallet that is not his and turns it in to the lost and found.

_____

10 Brian makes sure he checks his backpack every evening and gives his mom any important papers, and then he puts his finished homework in it.

_____

Name _____ Date _____

Interviewing the Captain

Based on your reading of the passage, prepare five questions you would ask Bill Pinkney if you could interview him. Then write the answer you think he would give to each question.

1 Question: _____

Answer: _____

_____

2 Question: _____

Answer: _____

_____

3 Question: _____

Answer: _____

_____

4 Question: _____

Answer: _____

_____

5 Question: _____

Answer: _____

_____

Writing a Biography

Imagine that you are going to write a biography of Bill Pinkney. Circle the items that would be important to include. Cross out the details that would not be important to include.

1 Bill Pinkney does not like diet soda.

2 Bill Pinkney has two grandchildren.

3 Bill Pinkney captained a replica of the *Amistad* from 2000 to 2004.

4 Bill Pinkney created an exhibit for the Chicago Museum of Science and Industry called "Winds of Change: Africa, the Americas, and the Sea."

5 Bill Pinkney has one daughter.

6 Bill Pinkney has a gold earring, which is in honor of his success rounding Cape Horn.

7 Bill Pinkney admires Michael Jordan.

8 Bill Pinkney's mother is one of his heroes.

9 Bill Pinkney lives in Chicago.

10 Bill Pinkney attended the Black Boater's Summit in 2000.

Nonfiction Reading Comprehension • 5–6 © 2005 Creative Teaching Press

Walt Whitman

"O Captain! My Captain!" are the opening lines to a famous poem. It was written after the assassination of Abraham Lincoln. It is a symbolic poem in which the captain of the ship brings it safely into port but dies before he can be welcomed by the crowds just as Lincoln was killed after bringing the country through the Civil War. It was written by a poet who had seen the devastation of that war firsthand, Walt Whitman.

Walt Whitman was born in New York on Long Island in 1819. His family later moved to Brooklyn and then back to Long Island. As a young man, Whitman learned the printing business. At that job, he learned to love reading. He worked a number of jobs—as a teacher, farmer, and carpenter—but he was always a writer. Between 1838 and 1859, he wrote for several different newspapers. He also had a few stories and poems published.

Though he did not fight in the conflict himself, the Civil War had a profound effect on Whitman. In 1862, Whitman's brother George was listed among the missing after the Battle of Fredericksburg. Whitman left Long Island to go find him. He ended up finding a purpose for his life—visiting the sick and wounded. He went to Washington, D.C., where he got a job in the Department of the Interior as a clerk. In his free time, he was a volunteer with the Christian Commission. He made over six hundred visits to hospitals, helping to treat the patients and listening to their stories. He may have helped as many as 100,000 people in the three remaining years of the war. Through it all, he continued to write.

He published a small book of poetry called *Drum Taps* in 1865.

This was not Whitman's first volume of poetry. In 1855, he had paid to publish twelve poems in a book called *Leaves of Grass*. It did not become very popular at the time. Its free verse style was very different from much of the other poetry of the day. He did send a copy to Ralph Waldo Emerson, a famous writer and poet, who thought it was very good and predicted that Whitman would be a very successful poet. Whitman must have been encouraged by Emerson's praise. The following year, he published a second edition of *Leaves of Grass* that included twenty more poems. Before his death, Whitman would publish nine different editions of the book. It changed as Whitman's life changed, but it also changed as America changed. His work was read outside of the United States, too. In fact, his early success came in countries such as England and Denmark, not the U.S.

Leaves of Grass proved to be the end of his Washington career. Whitman's boss, James Harlan, thought that the poems were indecent, and when Harlan found out Whitman was the author, he fired him in 1873. Whitman went to his brother's house in Camden, New Jersey, to visit his dying mother. There he suffered a stroke, which would somewhat limit what he could do for the rest of his life. He did manage to keep writing. More editions of *Leaves of Grass* were published. Famous writers, such as Oscar Wilde and Alfred Lord Tennyson, came to visit him. His last book of poetry was *Good-Bye My Fancy*. He died on March 26, 1892, and was buried in Camden.

Another of Whitman's famous poems is "I Hear America Singing." In it, he talks about a mechanic, a shoemaker, and even a girl sewing. His poetry was meant for the everyday American, and most adult Americans can recognize themselves in some of the words he wrote.

Words of Whitman

Unscramble the words to complete each sentence.

1 The suffering he saw had a **noufdrop** effect on Whitman.
_____

2 His boss fired Whitman for writing **teencind** poetry. _____

3 The poem "O Captain! My Captain" was **byslicom** of Lincoln's assassination.
_____

4 Whitman could not believe the **avesttodian** he saw at Fredericksburg.
_____

5 People were not used to Whitman's style of **reef serve**.
_____

6 Whitman had **strifnahd** knowledge about the printing business.
_____

7 Another name for a book is a **ulmove**. _____

8 Whitman was saddened by the **ssssaaanniiot** of President Lincoln._____

9 Whitman was not a soldier in the **cliftcon**. _____

10 There were nine **stoidine** of *Leaves of Grass*. _____

Nonfiction Reading Comprehension • 5–6 © 2005 Creative Teaching Press

A Sample of Whitman's Life

Using the passage, fill in the events that happened in each year of Whitman's life.

1 1819 _____

2 1838 _____

3 1855 _____

4 1856 _____

5 1859 _____

6 1862 _____

7 1865 _____

8 1873 _____

9 1892 _____

Name _____ Date _____

Whitman's Ideas

Look at the main idea sentences in the box. Choose the main idea for each set of details.

> Whitman loved to write.
> Whitman understood the common people of America.
> Other writers respected Whitman's work.
> Family was important to Whitman.

① _____

- Whitman worked as a teacher, carpenter, and farmer.
- Whitman spent time with soldiers in the hospital.
- Whitman wrote about mechanics and shoemakers.

② _____

- Whitman went to find his missing brother.
- Whitman went to visit his dying mother.
- Whitman lived near his brother in Camden, New Jersey.

③ _____

- Whitman worked for several newspapers.
- Whitman published nine different editions of *Leaves of Grass.*
- Whitman wrote *Drum Taps* and *Good-Bye My Fancy.*

④ _____

- Oscar Wilde came to visit Whitman.
- Ralph Waldo Emerson liked *Leaves of Grass*.
- Whitman was visited by Alfred Lord Tennyson.

Nonfiction Reading Comprehension • 5–6 © 2005 Creative Teaching Press

Gwendolyn Brooks

"Very early in life I became fascinated with the wonders language can achieve. And I began playing with words," said poet Gwendolyn Brooks. Indeed, her mother, a schoolteacher, noticed her talent when Gwendolyn was only seven years old, and she encouraged her by sharing many different types of literature with her. Her family also encouraged her writing by giving her a special desk and by allowing her to skip chores in order to write. Gwendolyn did not have many friends when she was growing up, so she spent a lot of time by herself, reading and writing. At the age of eleven, she began sending poems about her family to a local newspaper. When she was only thirteen years old, Gwendolyn Brooks had her poem, "Eventide," published in *American Childhood Magazine.* Only four years later, she had published nearly 100 poems in a weekly column she wrote for the *Chicago Defender.*

Gwendolyn Brooks was born June 7, 1917, in Topeka, Kansas, but six weeks later her mother took her back to the South Side of Chicago, Illinois, where Gwendolyn lived most of her life. She attended three different high schools—one comprised mostly of white students, one that consisted of all black students, and one that was integrated. These experiences with people of different races as well as her experiences

living in black neighborhoods influenced her poetry.

In 1936, Brooks received her English degree from Wilson Junior College. She married Henry Blakely in 1938, and their son Henry Jr. was born in 1940. During this time, she kept writing as much poetry as she could. After Henry Jr.'s birth, she became involved with a poetry workshop taught by Inez Cunningham Stark at the South Side Community Art Center. With the other writers' help and encouragement, her poetry improved. She received her first major award, the Midwestern Writers Conference Poetry Award in 1943.

Her first book of poetry, *A Street in Bronzeville,* was published in 1945. It led to her being named one of the "Ten Young Women of the Year" by *Mademoiselle* magazine. In 1950, Gwendolyn Brooks became the first black writer to win a Pulitzer Prize. It was for her second book of poems, *Annie Allen*, which had been published in 1949.

In 1961, ten years after the birth of her daughter Nora, Brooks began teaching American literature at the University of Chicago. She began teaching poetry at Chicago's Columbia College in 1963. In 1968, she was appointed poet laureate of the state of Illinois. To encourage young people to write poetry, she established the Illinois Poet Laureate Awards in 1969.

Brooks read her poetry at the Library of Congress poetry festival in 1962, at the request of President John F. Kennedy. Twenty-three years later, she became its poetry consultant. She received a lifetime achievement award from the National Endowment for the Arts in 1989. In 1994, she received the highest humanities award the federal government can give.

Gwendolyn Brooks died in Chicago on December 3, 2000. Friends and family were gathered around her, taking turns reading to her. Her love of language continued to the very end of her life.

Nonfiction Reading Comprehension • 5–6 © 2005 Creative Teaching Press

Name _____ Date _____

Kinds of Poetry

ballad	blank verse	couplet	doggerel	elegy
epic	free verse	haiku	ode	poem
refrain	rhyme	rhythm	sonnet	verse

Use the words from the box to complete the crossword puzzle.

Across

2. sad poem
4. feelings or ideas expressed in rhythmic language
5. long poem that tells a heroic story
7. poetry that doesn't rhyme
10. Japanese, unrhymed poem
11. repeated verse or phrase
13. poem that tells a story, written like a song
14. rhythmic lines of writing
15. stressed and unstressed syllables that make a pattern

Down

1. poetry that is crude or not well-written
3. poetry that varies in rhythm pattern or line length
6. two lines of poetry that go together
8. fourteen-line poem with a specific structure and rhyming pattern
9. similar sounds at the ends of lines of poetry
12. poem, written like a song, that has lots of emotion

Poetry

Gwendolyn Brooks enjoyed discovering new writers and helping young people find the poetry in their own lives. Here are some of her words about poetry:

- "When I'm excited about something or moved by something, I take notes on it immediately so I won't forget or lose my inspiration."
- "I write and rewrite and ask myself the sterling question—Is this really what I want to say? With an emphasis on *really* and *I*."
- "In December 1967, at a workshop called the Kumuba Workshop in a rundown theater in Chicago, I was given an award for just being me, and that's what poetry is to me—just being me." (That award meant more to her than any other.)

Write a poem of your own.

1. Choose a topic that you are excited about or that moves you emotionally.
2. Imagine you are a reporter describing your topic for an audience.
3. Avoid phrases everybody uses like "white as snow" or "hot as an oven."
4. Make sure you are saying what you really want to say about your topic.
5. Rewrite.
6. Try to create your own form of poetry.
7. Just be yourself.

My topic: _____

Why I chose this topic: _____

How I feel about this topic: _____

Words I can use to describe my topic: _____

_____

Nonfiction Reading Comprehension • 5–6 © 2005 Creative Teaching Press

Name _____ Date _____

Becoming a Poet

Several things led to Gwendolyn Brooks becoming a poet. Circle the things that helped her become a writer. Cross out the things that did not help her become a poet.

1 She was born in Topeka, Kansas.

2 Her father was the son of a runaway slave.

3 She had a younger brother named Raymond.

4 Her mother read to her.

5 Her family gave her a special place to write.

6 She got a job with the *Chicago Defender*.

7 She worked as a cleaning woman.

8 She met famous poets James Weldon Johnson and Langston Hughes, who encouraged her.

9 She received over fifty honorary degrees from colleges and universities.

10 She was very shy.

Nonfiction Reading Comprehension • 5–6 © 2005 Creative Teaching Press

Ragtime

It is hard to describe, but you know it when you hear it. It is a truly American form of music. The popular music we enjoy on the radio today has its roots in this turn-of-the-century musical phenomenon, known as ragtime.

No one is sure exactly where and when ragtime got its start. Around the late 1890s, it became popular with African American pianists who traveled up and down the Mississippi River and the surrounding areas. They provided dance music at a number of gathering places. Ragtime developed its own distinctive, syncopated style, which first captured some notice at the time of the World's Fair in Chicago in 1893. One of the composers who would become best known for ragtime songs was there at the time—Scott Joplin.

The three "fathers" of American ragtime were Scott Joplin, James Scott, and Joseph Lamb. In addition to them, the contributions of John Stark, owner of the music publisher Stark and Sons, cannot be ignored. They were responsible for getting published copies of the composers' sheet music out to the general public and increasing ragtime's popularity.

Joseph Lamb was born in Montclair, New Jersey, in 1887. He was Irish, not African American as were the other notable ragtime composers of the time. He learned to play piano when he was young, but he went to college to study engineering. He continued to write music while there and had several "rags" published in the early 1900s. It was after he went to work for a New York publisher that he met his idol, Scott Joplin. He impressed Joplin enough with his playing that Joplin introduced him to John Stark. Lamb continued playing ragtime professionally until about 1914. He died in 1960.

James Scott was born on February 12, 1885, in Neosho, Missouri, the son of a former slave. He, too, learned music at a young age and showed an amazing talent for it. By 1901, Scott was a talented player of ragtime, as well as classical and popular music. He began working for the Dumars Music Company, and they published his first rag in 1903. He began studying with Scott Joplin in 1906. Joplin also introduced Scott to John Stark, who published Scott's work as well. The development of jazz in the 1920s eventually edged out ragtime, much to Scott's dismay. There was no longer a market for his music. Fortunately, some of his rags have been preserved on player piano rolls. He died on August 30, 1938.

Scott Joplin was born around the end of 1867, somewhere in northeast Texas, the son of a former slave. He probably learned to play the piano in the home of a white family for whom his mother worked. Throughout the late 1880s, Joplin traveled all over the United States, playing with various musical groups. Most of the time, he was centered around the areas of Sedalia and St. Louis, Missouri. In 1899, he published his most famous piece of music, the "Maple Leaf Rag", named for a club in Sedalia. Joplin suffered a nervous breakdown in 1911, which eventually led to his admission to a mental hospital in 1916. He died there on April 1, 1917. His death would signal the end of the ragtime era. During his lifetime, Joplin's music was popular, but he was not taken seriously as a composer. The use of "The Entertainer" in the movie *The Sting* in the early 1970s revived interest in his music. His genius was finally recognized with a posthumous Pulitzer Prize in 1976.

Though the ragtime era only lasted for approximately twenty years, it is significant in the history of American music. It was the first truly American form of music to be published. One only has to turn on the radio and listen to the heavy bass line and syncopation of rap music to know that ragtime's influence continues even to this day.

Timely Vocabulary

Unscramble the words to complete each sentence.

1 There were **roivaus** pianists playing ragtime music in the 1890s.
_____

2 Joplin, Scott, and Lamb were famous **processom** of ragtime.
_____

3 The rhythms of ragtime are **viscinttide.** _____

4 The **troiluappy** of ragtime music made people want to buy copies of the music.
_____

5 Joplin was **dresspime** with the playing of Scott and Lamb.
_____

6 Ragtime was a turn-of-the-century **nnnooeemph.** _____

7 John Stark's **birtutscionon** to ragtime came from publishing the rags.
_____

8 A **thoosumpus** award is given after a person is dead.
_____

9 African American **stainsip** are most responsible for developing ragtime.
_____

10 Ragtime rhythms were **stancopyed.** _____

11 There was a ragtime **livavre** in the 1950s and again in the 1970s.
_____

Nonfiction Reading Comprehension • 5–6 © 2005 Creative Teaching Press

Name _____ Date _____

Popular Music

Use the chart to compare your favorite kind of music with ragtime.

	Ragtime	
Instruments		
Musicians		
Characteristics of music		
How people enjoy it		

Use the information in the chart to write a comparison essay.

_____

_____

_____

_____

_____

_____

_____

_____

_____

_____

_____

_____

Nonfiction Reading Comprehension • 5–6 © 2005 Creative Teaching Press

Name _____ Date _____

Because of Ragtime

Fill in the missing causes and effects to complete the chart.

Cause	Effect
1 People came to the Chicago World Fair from all over the world.	
2 Ragtime was good dance music, and people liked to dance.	
3 John Stark and Sons published ragtime music.	
4	Joseph Lamb met his idol Scott Joplin.
5 Joplin introduced Scott and Lamb to John Stark.	
6 James Scott started working for the Dumars Music Company.	
7 Jazz developed in the 1920s.	
8 Joplin's mother worked for a white family.	
9 Joplin died in a mental hospital.	
10	Interest in ragtime music was renewed.

Nonfiction Reading Comprehension • 5–6 © 2005 Creative Teaching Press

What Does a Conductor Do?

There is one job that almost every one of us has pretended to do. It isn't being a firefighter or a doctor. For some, it may not seem like much of a job at all. How hard can it be to stand up in front of a bunch of musicians and wave your arms? It doesn't seem that complicated, but an orchestra conductor has one of the most challenging jobs in the world.

An orchestra conductor has to get more than one hundred people to work together at the same time to create something beautiful. It is not always easy. He may have people working for him who have far more years of experience than he does. It is almost certain that the conductor could not play the instrument as well as the musician, but he has to tell the musician what to do. Most orchestral scores do not give specific directions about exactly how the composer expected them to be played. It is the job of the conductor to interpret the music and to get the orchestra to go along with that interpretation.

The job of conductor did not exist before the early 1800s. During the Baroque Period, the musicians were led by either the person playing the harpsichord, a keyboard instrument, or by the first violinist. If the players needed help keeping time, the composer might pound the floor with a stick to maintain the beat, or he might tap a rolled-up piece of sheet music on

the music stand. Either way, it probably interfered with people's enjoyment of the music. For composer Jean Baptiste Lully, the stick pounding proved fatal. He missed the floor and stabbed his foot. It caused an infection that killed him.

As Ludwig Van Beethoven's music ushered in the Romantic Period, it became necessary to have a conductor who could help the musicians interpret the music. Unlike Baroque music, which followed strict rules, Romantic music was more about making connections with the listener. Beethoven's student Louis Spohr was probably the first person to conduct an orchestra the way we think about the job today.

Some composers, hoping to get their music to sound the way they wanted, became conductors. Leonard Bernstein, Gustav Mahler, Richard Strauss, and Richard Wagner were all composers and conductors. More recently, John Williams, the composer of the *Star Wars* and *Harry Potter* theme music and many other film scores, is well-known for conducting the Boston Pops Orchestra.

Probably one of the most famous conductors of modern times was Arturo Toscanini. He was an extremely demanding but very gifted conductor. Because he was very nearsighted, he had to memorize every score he conducted.

Making music is not the only part of a conductor's job. Conductors must be in charge of much of the business of the orchestra. They need to choose what music the orchestra will play, make sure enough copies are purchased, and write the notes about the music for the program. They must arrange for guest musicians and soloists. They may be responsible for hiring and firing the musicians. Most importantly, they must be involved in raising money for the group since orchestras are expensive to run.

If you enjoy music and a challenge, you may want to consider becoming an orchestra conductor someday. It is a demanding profession, but when done correctly, it produces very satisfying results.

Nonfiction Reading Comprehension • 5–6 © 2005 Creative Teaching Press

Name _____ Date _____

Musical Words

accelerando	adagio	allegro	andante	con
crescendo	da capo	diminuendo	fine	lento
molto	presto	sforzando	tutti	vivace

Match each musical term with its definition. Use a dictionary if you need help.

1 very fast tempo ___ ___ ___ ___ ___ ___

2 fast tempo ___ ___ ___ ___ ___ ___

3 suddenly loud ___ ___ ___ ___ ___ ___ ___ ___

4 back to the beginning ___ ___ ___ ___ ___ ___

5 getting faster ___ ___ ___ ___ ___ ___ ___ ___ ___ ___ ___

6 all together ___ ___ ___ ___ ___

7 the end ___ ___ ___ ___

8 getting softer ___ ___ ___ ___ ___ ___ ___ ___ ___ ___

9 getting louder ___ ___ ___ ___ ___ ___ ___ ___ ___

10 slow and leisurely ___ ___ ___ ___ ___ ___

11 lively ___ ___ ___ ___ ___ ___

12 with ___ ___ ___

13 very ___ ___ ___ ___ ___

14 walking tempo ___ ___ ___ ___ ___ ___ ___

15 slow ___ ___ ___ ___ ___

Nonfiction Reading Comprehension • 5–6 © 2005 Creative Teaching Press

Name _____ Date _____

Orchestra Seating

Read the information about where the parts of the orchestra are seated. Use the names in bold to label each section of the diagram.

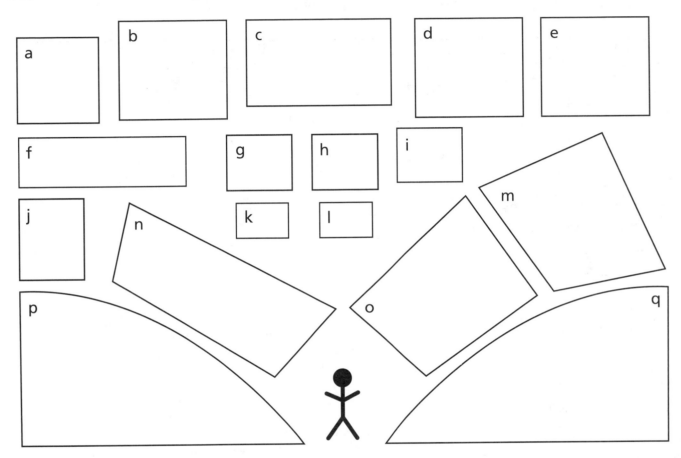

- The **first violins** are on the conductor's left as he is facing the orchestra.
- The **cellos** are on the conductor's right.
- The **second** violins are behind the first violins.
- The **violas** are behind the cellos.
- The **harp** is behind the first violins and to the left of the second violins.
- The **double basses** are behind the cellos and to the right of the violas.
- The **flutes** and **piccolos** are between the second violins and violas on the left.
- The **oboes** are between the second violins and violas on the right.
- The **clarinets** are behind the flutes.
- The **bassoons** are behind the oboes.
- The **trumpets** are to the right of the bassoons.
- The **trombones** are behind the trumpets.
- The **tubas** are to the right of the trombones.
- The **French horns** are behind the harp and second violins and to the left of the clarinets.
- The **timpani** are behind the clarinets and bassoons.
- The **percussion** are to the left of the timpani.
- The **piano** is behind the French horns and to the left of the percussion.

Name _____ Date _____

What Did He Say?

The famous Italian conductor Carlos Conductorini has come to be a guest conductor for the orchestra. Unfortunately, his English is not very good, and if he doesn't know the word he needs, he just skips it. Fill in the blanks to complete Carlos' description of his day.

I got up in the _____ at 6:00 a.m. I ate
(1)

_____ with my _____ and then got
(2)   (3)

_____.
(4)

I took a _____ to the _____ to meet
(5)   (6)

with the musicians. The _____ were locked.
(7)

I _____ I had the wrong _____. I saw a
(8)   (9)

man and _____ him if this was the _____.
(10)   (11)

He said it was, so I _____ on the _____.
(12)   (13)

Someone came to the _____ and let me in.
(14)

The musicians were _____ in their seats with their instru-
(15)

ments. We _____ at the music we were going to play that
(16)

_____. I lifted my baton and we _____ to
(17)   (18)

rehearse. They _____ wonderful! We were
(19)

_____ before lunchtime.
(20)

That _____ all the seats in the _____
(21)   (22)

were full. We played a _____ concert and everyone smiled and
(23)

_____. My trip to this country has been
(24)

_____ good!
(25)

Nonfiction Reading Comprehension • 5–6 © 2005 Creative Teaching Press

Texture in Art

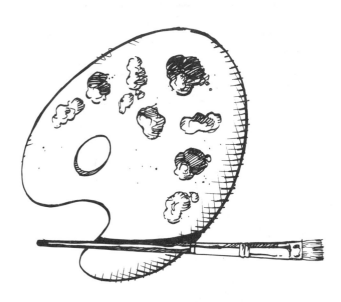

What does a piece of velvet feel like? What about the bark of a tree or a grassy field? We know through our sense of touch what these textures are like. It is easy to create texture in art that we can touch. The difficult job for an artist is to create a picture so lifelike that we can feel the velvet or the tree bark or the grass even though we are only looking at the picture with our eyes.

For a long time, artists had difficulty with the idea of creating texture in two-dimensional paintings. How could the artists imply texture in a smooth painting? Before 1420, it was nearly impossible for artists to show texture. The paint they used, tempera, was made with pigment, water, and egg yolk and was very thin. It gave bright colors to the painting but no texture. That changed with Jan and Hubert van Eyck, two brothers who were artists in Holland and Belgium. They took a new idea, mixing oil with the pigment, and used it in their art. Suddenly, it was possible to create the layers of paint necessary to give art texture.

Texture in art got another big boost from a different Dutch artist over four hundred years later. Vincent van Gogh, inspired by the Impressionists, started painting in 1880, using bright colors and different kinds of paint textures.

Texture became an important element in his paintings such as *Wheat Fields Under Thunder Clouds*, and *The Starry Night*. He only sold one painting before his death in 1890, but van Gogh's bold strokes would forever influence the art world.

Another Impressionist artist who experimented with the use of texture was Mary Cassatt. She was an American who came to Paris in 1874. Her subjects were mostly women and children in everyday life. She used texture to suggest contrasts between such things as skin, porcelain, and fabric in *The Child's Bath*.

Texture for the sake of texture alone was part of the work of Jackson Pollock. During the 1940s and 1950s, he was known for creating huge canvases by dripping or pouring paint onto them. To create even more texture, he would combine sand, glass, keys, and other things with the paint.

Using oil paints can be messy and may not be the best way for you to create your own art with texture. Fortunately, there is an easier way. Collage is a form of art that you have probably been making since you were old enough to use scissors and a glue stick. Construction paper, however, is not a medium with a lot of texture. Artists use a variety of materials to create texturally rich collages. They can be natural materials, such as bark and leaves, or man-made materials like foil and cellophane. Collages are a great way to recycle materials, too.

Another simple texture technique was introduced by Max Ernst around 1925. It is called *frottage*. It is when you put a sheet of paper over a textured object and rub a pencil or crayon over it until the image of the texture is transferred to the paper. Have you ever done that before?

Texture draws the observers into a piece of art and allows them to bring their sense of touch to their understanding of the artwork. It gives energy to art. A lot of artists have used texture, but the full use of texture in art is still waiting to be explored.

Nonfiction Reading Comprehension • 5–6 © 2005 Creative Teaching Press

Words with Feeling

bumpy	fleecy	fluffy	furry	fuzzy
nubby	prickly	rough	silky	smooth
lacy	velvety	grainy		

Find the texture words from the box in the word search.

```
E  Q  P  P  E  H  Y  L  K  C  I  R  P  A  H
W  F  M  O  L  N  T  F  U  R  R  Y  U  C  P
V  I  R  S  I  M  E  O  F  B  N  U  L  D  G
Q  Z  L  A  S  N  V  F  O  U  A  V  Q  X  M
Q  Z  R  X  X  P  L  Q  L  M  L  V  J  R  H
N  G  O  N  B  E  E  A  Y  P  S  F  R  N  H
U  R  X  D  E  H  V  N  C  Y  W  B  L  D  Q
X  M  N  C  K  D  Q  C  X  Y  F  V  K  P  P
I  Y  Y  Z  Z  U  F  A  R  S  J  E  A  W  S
L  F  K  B  U  P  A  R  Z  N  U  R  N  P  Q
G  X  L  F  B  Q  O  W  L  T  T  P  K  S  N
O  Z  I  W  S  U  E  M  P  H  R  T  O  D  W
Z  R  S  U  G  E  N  N  C  U  V  E  S  M  K
Q  T  F  H  T  E  S  R  S  R  L  H  Q  P  O
H  V  U  C  P  F  W  L  H  M  I  I  A  I  T
```

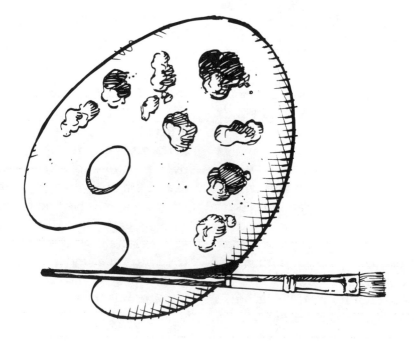

Name _____ Date _____

Feelings

bumpy	fleecy	fluffy	furry	fuzzy
nubby	prickly	rough	silky	smooth
grainy	velvety	lacy		

Use the table to put the texture words in groups that seem to go together. There are many possible ways to group them. Use as many boxes as you need. You may also add words of your own that fit each category.

1	2	3
4	**5**	**6**

Describe why you put each set of words together. If you did not use all of the boxes, leave the lines blank.

1 _____
_____

2 _____
_____

3 _____
_____

4 _____
_____

5 _____
_____

6 _____
_____

Nonfiction Reading Comprehension • 5–6 © 2005 Creative Teaching Press

New Masterpieces

New art masterpieces have just been discovered. Use the passage to help you determine which artist created each piece of artwork.

 _____

② _____

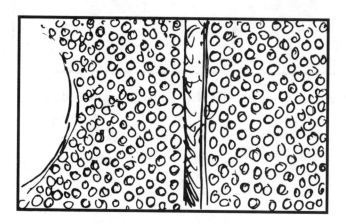

 _____

④ _____

⑤ _____

 _____

Tricksters

We have been aware of him since we were small children and our parents first began reading us stories. He was the character who was smart, but not too smart. He was like us, often getting in trouble and learning an important lesson in the process. No matter what culture we grew up in, the trickster was there.

Heroes are always exciting to read about, but they didn't show up in tales until about 9,000 years ago. Tricksters, on the other hand, can be found beginning about 20,000 years ago, and may go all the way back to humans' first attempts to tell stories.

We like trickster stories for many reasons, mostly because tricksters remind us of ourselves. They are basically good, but sometimes their selfishness gets in the way. When they do something they shouldn't, they usually get caught and have to make up for it. Like us, many times the tricksters just can't help their behavior. Their intelligence makes them curious and their curiosity gets them in trouble. Fortunately, that same intelligence often helps them get out of trouble. Sometimes they may have the ability to change shapes or have other supernatural powers. Often they aren't human at all.

Native American and African stories are full of tricksters. Native American characters were usually animals. Blue Jay was the trickster the Chinook tribe talked about. Raven, Fox, Mink, Seagull, and Rabbit were all considered tricky fellows by others, but probably the best known of all was Coyote. According to legend, we have him to thank for the stars in the sky, even though he got his tail singed in the process.

In African stories, Tortoise gets into its share of mischief. Because a tortoise lives so long, it has gained a lot of wisdom even though it doesn't move very quickly. Unfortunately, he doesn't always use that wisdom in the way he should. He gets in trouble when he puts his own desires above the needs of the community. He teaches us important lessons, such as we need to learn to work together if we want to survive.

Ananzi the spider is probably the best known of the African tricksters. Ananzi often has run-ins with the Great Spirit. Like other tricksters, we learn from Ananzi not to mess with forces greater than we are.

Many of these animal characters eventually end up benefiting their human neighbors. Without them, we might not be living on Earth. We might not have fire for warmth or corn to eat or music to listen to.

Other tricksters are more god-like. Wisagatcak, described by the Cree tribe, accidentally flooded the world but then saved all of the animals on a large raft. In Greek mythology, Hermes really was a god, but his job as messenger for the rest of the gods and goddesses gave him plenty of chances for mischief. Further north, Loki created trouble with the other gods in Norse myths. He had a talent for getting them to forgive him time and time again. They probably shouldn't have given him so many chances. In the end, he was the one who destroyed their world.

One of the few fully human tricksters is Till Eulenspiegel. In German literature, he does a wonderful job of fooling those people who think far too much of themselves, like the pompous professors at a university. He is like so many characters we root for now on television—the little guy who manages to come out on top by making others see how foolish the popular guys are.

Tricksters give us a chance to be entertained, but they also teach us a little something about ourselves. We can learn from their mistakes.

Nonfiction Reading Comprehension • 5–6 © 2005 Creative Teaching Press

Tricky Words

Some words are often confused. Take a look at each tricky pair and write the correct word in each sentence.

allowed   aloud

1 We are not _____ to go with you.

2 The teacher read the story _____.

dessert   desert

3 I would like more _____, please.

4 Be sure to take water if you are traveling in the _____.

do   due

5 Your homework assignment is _____ tomorrow.

6 Can you _____ it by yourself?

knew   new

7 We _____ it would be difficult.

8 Are those _____ shoes you are wearing?

know   no

9 I _____ you understand what I am saying.

10 I have _____ idea what you are talking about.

past   passed

11 We will leave at half _____ four.

12 She _____ me the ball.

quite   quiet

13 You gave me _____ a scare.

14 It is too _____ in there.

then   than

15 She is older _____ he is.

16 And _____ I heard the phone ring.

who's   whose

17 _____ going to pick me up after school?

18 He didn't know _____ shoes they were.

your   you're

19 _____ welcome to join us for dinner.

20 Is that _____ book on the table?

Nonfiction Reading Comprehension • 5–6 © 2005 Creative Teaching Press

Comparing Characters

Use information from the passage to complete the Venn diagram to compare tricksters and humans.

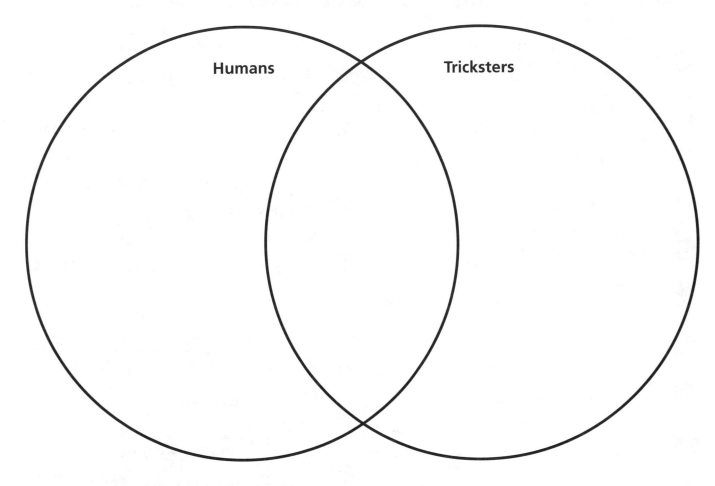

Use the information you listed above to complete the paragraphs.

Tricksters and humans are the same in some ways. They both _____

_____

_____

_____

_____

Tricksters and humans are different. They _____

_____

_____

_____

_____

The Trick of Writing a Good Story

Trickster stories contain specific elements. Use the passage to help you determine what might be in a trickster tale. Circle the elements that a trickster tale might have. Cross out elements that would not be part of a trickster tale.

1 supernatural powers

2 space aliens

3 foolish people

4 lesson learned

5 gods and goddesses

6 explanation for why things are the way they are

7 talking animals

8 punishment

9 true-to-life situations

10 mystery to be solved

11 humor

12 good fairy

13 setting in nature

14 handsome prince

15 talking vehicles

Nonfiction Reading Comprehension • 5–6 © 2005 Creative Teaching Press

Answer Key

Out of This World (page 6)

1. galaxy
2. radiation
3. core
4. universe
5. poles
6. supernova
7. x-ray
8. pulsar
9. atom
10. supergiant
11. fusion
12. neutron star
13. theory
14. pressure
15. accretion disk
Answer to the riddle: Neptunes

Name That Star (page 7)

1. c
2. b
3. d
4. h
5. e
6. a
7. f
8. i
9. g

How Does It Happen? (page 8)

A massive star begins to run out of fuel.
The star begins to develop a core of iron.
The iron cannot be compressed any more.
The star explodes in a supernova.
The leftovers of the star begin collapsing.
Gravity is so strong that the object keeps collapsing.
A black hole is formed.

A Black Hole (page 9)

Answers will vary.

Astronaut or Cosmonaut? (page 11)

1. aero-; atmo-; helio-; luni-; stelli-
2. acous-; gluc-; oculo-; oro-; oto-
3. avi-; cyto-; ichthyo-; phyto-; rhizo-
4. andro-; anthropo-; ethno-; pedo-
5. centi-; deca-; dodeca-; hepta-; hexa-; septi-; uni-

Dogs or Monkeys (page 12)

Answers may vary. Possible answers include:
Dogs
Good things about using them
They are plentiful.
They can be easily trained.
They are not expensive.
Bad things about using them
They can't do everything a human can.
Most are bigger than monkeys.
They can't communicate like some chimps.

Monkeys and Chimpanzees
Good things about using them
They are a lot like humans.
They can be easily trained.
Some can communicate in sign language.
Bad things about using them
They are difficult to obtain.
They can be expensive.
They are too much like humans; we would feel worse if
    something happened to them.

Paragraphs will vary.

Visual Aids (page 13)

1. Laika became first dog in space.
2. First monkey in space.
3. Ham was first chimp in space.
4. Zvezdochka the dog tested procedure for human flight.
5. Yuri Gagarin is first human in space.
6. Alan Shepard is first American in space.
7. Gherman Titov stays in space 25 hours and 18 minutes.
8. John Glenn orbits the Earth.
9. Valentina Tereshkova becomes first woman in space.
10. Valentina Tereshkova
11. Gherman Titov
12. John Glenn
13. Yuri Gagarin
14. Alan Shepherd

Animal Babies (page 15)

Across
6. poult
7. calf
9. kitten
10. eyas
12. gosling
14. cygnet
18. puggle

19. cub
20. chick
21. pup
22. fry
23. leveret
24. whelp

Down
1. squab
2. hatchling
3. ephyna
4. kit
5. fingerling
8. fawn
9. kid
11. joey
13. foal
14. cockerel
15. tadpole
16. pinkie
17. pullet
20. cria

3. labour
4. nursery
5. gaggle
6. aerie
7. bevy
8. congress
9. army
10. sleuth
11. pride
12. kindle
13. knot
14. flock
15. crash
16. murder
17. rookery
18. clutter
19. business
20. pod
21. shiver
22. skulk
23. ambush

Why Do They Do That? (page 16)

1. They eat other birds.
   They nest on cliff ledges.
   It is the fastest flying bird.
2. They live in desert climates.
   They eat rodents.
   They have good eyesight and hearing.
3. They do not have any natural defenses.
   They have large ears and eyes.
4. They live in groups for protection.
   They have large eyes.
   They live in burrows.
5. Some have black fur.
   They have good eyesight.
6. They spend most of their time in trees.

Say It Again (page 17)

Answers will vary.

Active Animals (page 18)

1. nocturnal
2. diurnal
3. nocturnal
4. crepuscular (nocturnal is also acceptable)

Animal Groups (page 20)

1. array
2. charm

Comparing Crowns (page 21)

Answers will vary.

Who's Who? (page 22)

1. horns
2. tusks
3. horns
4. antlers
5. antlers
6. tusks

Which Would You Want? (page 23)

Answers will vary.

Math Words (page 25)

equation	ray	mixed number
factor	variable	inequality
parallel lines	perimeter	obtuse angle
mean	symmetry	equivalent fractions
circumference	acute angle	chord
mode	radius	median
area	improper fraction	diameter

A Letter to the World (page 26)

Answers may vary.

Weather Words (page 28)

1. l
2. n
3. d
4. f
5. j
6. e
7. a
8. g
9. b
10. m
11. c
12. h
13. k
14. i

Build Your Own Barometer (page 29)

1. a vacuum
2. Answers may vary. Possible answers include: It can bend easily as the pressure changes and is airtight.
3. yes
4. Answers may vary. Possible answers include: The air inside the can would expand. Pressure is affected by temperature.
5. rising—Explanations may vary. Possible answers include: When there is more pressure, the air in the can contracts. This causes the plastic wrap to get sucked into the can and the straw points up.
6. falling— Explanations may vary. Possible answers include: When there is less pressure, the air in the can expands. This makes the plastic wrap bulge and the straw point dip down.

Predicting the Weather (page 30)

1. yes
2. no
3. yes

Climate Words (page 32)

1. tropical
2. Mediterranean
3. temperate
4. temperature
5. precipitation
6. tundra
7. taiga
8. hemispheres
9. grasslands
10. permafrost
11. elevation
12. desert
13. arid
14. equator
15. steppe

Matching Zones (page 33)

1. arid
2. tropical
3. temperate
4. polar
5. mountain (or high elevation)
6. Mediterranean
7. temperate
8. arid

What's Wrong with This Picture? (page 34)

1. Trees do not grow in the tundra.
2. You don't need a parka in a rain forest in the tropical zone.
3. It would not be raining in a polar zone.
4. Cactus don't grow in mountain zones.

My Zone (page 35)

Answers will vary. Make sure students have correctly identified their climate zone.

"Geo" Means Earth (page 37)

1. e
2. l
3. i
4. k
5. f
6. a
7. d
8. p
9. h
10. g
11. b
12. r
13. q
14. c
15. o
16. n
17. m
18. j

What Makes Them Move? (page 38)

Cross out sentences 2, 3, 6, 7, and 9.

What's Going On? (page 39)

Answers may vary. Possible answers include:
1. One plate is being subducted under another.
2. Two plates are colliding and creating a mountain range.
3. New crust is being formed under the ocean.
4. A fault is moving, causing an earthquake.

New Words (page 41)

Answers will vary.

New Year Map (page 43)

January or February: China, Hong Kong, Malaysia,
　　Singapore, Vietnam
March: Pakistan
mid-April: Burma, Cambodia, Laos, Sri Lanka, Thailand
October or November: India
changes from year to year: Iran

My New Year (page 44)

Answers will vary.

My Favorite Holiday (page 46)

Answers will vary.

Would You? (page 47)

Put a circle around 1, 3, 4, 6, 8, 10, 13, and 14
Answers may vary. Possible answers include:
#2—It is not a party. Everyone is welcome.
#5—Trees are not part of the celebration.
#7—You are supposed to be nice to each other.
#9—You are not supposed to get fancy. You should be
　　thankful for what you have.
#11—You are not supposed to get fancy.
#12—It is not supposed to be a big party. If there is music,
　　it is at the fairs.
#15—There are no candles involved in the holiday.

Finding Your Way (page 49)

1. trade routes
2. civilizations
3. merchants
4. goods
5. textiles
6. transported
7. trek
8. caravans
9. bandits
10. altitudes
11. arid
12. merchandise
13. rhubarb
14. uninhabited
15. technology

Changing History (page 50)

Answers will vary. Possible answers include:
1. The Silk Road became a popular trade route.
2. It was hard to find water in the arid lands.
3. The journey had a lot of risks and dangers.
4. Traders banded together in caravans.
5. Technology traveled eastward over the Silk Road.
6. Marco Polo wrote a book about his travels.
7. It took over a year to make the entire journey.
8. Use of the Silk Road as a trade route declined.
9. Buddhism became an important religion in China.
10. Travelers got stranded.

Does It Matter? (page 51)

Cross out sentences 1, 3, 5, 6, 7, 8, 10, and 12.

Synonym Search (page 53)

```
B A N P E S T I L E N C E
E C A T A C L Y S M E C B
M A F C A R N A G E N U A
I N F E S T A T I O N R N
C A L A M I T Y X F E S E
D C I S I T A D I O N E V
I N C A T A S T R O P H E
S S T R A G E D Y S M E X
A C I R S E R C A T A C A
S C O U R G E E N T F F T
T U N R Y M E X A L I T I
E R E P I D E M I C R O O
R S E D E C I M A T I O N
```

Staying Healthy (page 54)

Answers will vary. Possible answers include: Stay away from
　　rats and fleas. Don't go near sick people. Wash your
　　hands often.

Ring Around the Rosie (page 55)

1. d
2. b
3. c
4. a

Caches and Pirogues (page 57)

1. gauntlet
2. tippet
3. weirs
4. bezoar
5. sawyer
6. blunderbuss
7. pirogue
8. cache

9. cordelle
10. sniggle
11. clamons
12. pemmican

Say It Again (page 58)

Answers will vary.

Clark's Main Man (page 59)

Answers will vary. Possible answers include:
1. Your best friend becomes your master. York officially became William's property. York's wife had to remain with her master, and York stayed with Clark. York, as a slave, had no choice but to do as his master wished. York had to leave his wife to accompany Clark.
2. His strength was needed to help handle the twenty-three thousand pounds of goods the Corps took with them. York was an able hunter and was able to find other sources of food as well, such as watercress. York was even able to use the respect the Indians had for him to get food.
3. He and York became good friends as children. York was allowed to marry a slave woman from a neighboring plantation. Clark obviously valued York enough to want to include him in the adventure. Clark finally freed York.
4. When they saw a man who was entirely black, and whose color did not wash off, they were amazed. They referred to him as "Big Medicine," meaning they thought he had special spiritual power. York briefly got to share in the glory.   York had difficulty living as a free black man.

Artifacts (page 60)

1. keelboat
2. branding iron
3. bull boat
4. espontoon
5. Hadley's quadrant

Slang (page 62)

1. grassville
2. crib
3. roughs
4. squeal
5. wooden coat
6. patter
7. idea pot
8. barking irons
9. goaways
10. gapeseed

11. crusher
12. stepping ken
13. Richardsnary
14. polisher
15. sand
16. city college

Which Came First? (page 63)

1. b
2. b
3. a
4. b
5. a
6. a
7. b
8. b

Why Was It So Miserable? (page 64)

Answers will vary. Possible answers include:
1. There was a murder a night.
2. It was drained and made into a landfill.
3. Craftsmen couldn't stay in business.
4. It was built on a landfill.
5. Businesses moved out.
6. It was hard to get rid of human waste. Disease spread.
7. Children died at a high rate.
8. People consumed contaminated food and water.
9. There were rats and mice with fleas.
10. People lived in close quarters.

Terms to Know (page 66)

1. profitable
2. cultivator
3. furrows
4. manually
5. debris
6. continuation
7. expanding
8. textile
9. fertilize
10. mechanical
11. bolls
12. seedlings

How-to Book (page 67)

Put a circle around sentences 1, 3, 4, 6, 8, 9, 11, 13, and 15.
Cross out sentences 2, 5, 7, 10, 12, and 14.

A Letter to Cousin Jeb (page 68)

Answers will vary.

Civil War Medicine (page 70)

Across
1. dropsy
2. paroxysm
3. palsy
9. chilblain
10. ague
11. dresser
12. milk sickness
13. apoplexy
14. cramp colic

Down
1. diptheria
4. lumbago
5. consumption
6. bilious fever
7. lung fever
8. St. Vitus Dance
15. gripe

An Interview with the Doctor (page 71)

1. What were your views on women's clothing?
2. After the Civil War, you worked to get women the right to vote. Why did you think this was important?
3. Why do you think your medical practices were not successful?
4. How did you feel when they tried to take away your Medal of Honor?

Presenting to the Class (page 72)

Answers will vary.

Lincoln's Words (page 74)

1. score
2. conceived
3. liberty
4. dedicated
5. proposition
6. engaged
7. endure
8. propriety
9. consecrate
10. hallow
11. detract
12. task
13. honored
14. devotion
15. full measure
16. resolve
17. in vain
18. perish

But What Did It Mean? (page 75)

Answers will vary.

Writing Home (page 76)

Answers will vary.

Lincoln's Ideals (page 77)

1. agree
2. agree
3. disagree
4. agree
5. disagree
6. disagree
7. agree
8. disagree
9. agree
10. disagree
11. disagree
12. agree
13. disagree
14. agree
15. agree

Taking a "Krak" at Vocabulary (page 79)

Across
3. uneasy
4. submerged
9. tsunami
10. anticipation
11. pyroclastic flow
12. collapse
15. unpredictable

Down
1. inhabitants
2. radiating
4. stratosphere
5. cataclysm
6. subsided
7. filtered
8. magma chamber
13. extinct
14. engulfed
16. eruption

Dear Diary (page 80)

Answers will vary.

And Then What Happened? (page 81)

Answers may vary. Possible answers include:

1. Earthquakes began rumbling.
2. The sky got dark.
3. There was a lot of noise and dust shot into the air.
4. Krakatau was getting ready to erupt.
5. Krakatau collapsed.
6. Krakatau exploded.
7. People were killed.
8. Forty-foot tsunamis were created.
9. The sun appeared blue or green. Sunsets were redder. Temperatures dropped.
10. Volcanic activity continued in the area.

Parts of a Newspaper (page 83)

1. E. editorial
2. C. cut
3. H. photo credit
4. G. jumpline
5. D. dateline
6. F. head or headline
7. B. caption or cutline
8. A. byline

Five Ws and an H (page 84)

Answers will vary.

Headlines (page 85)

1. F
2. J
3. B
4. H
5. A
6. G
7. C
8. I
9. D
10. E

Kilroy Was Here (page 87)

1. gremlin
2. blitz
3. kamikaze
4. concentration camp
5. acronym
6. jeep
7. walkie-talkie
8. genocide

9. gung ho
10. dry run
11. radar
12. blockbuster
13. task force

Guilty or Not? (page 88)

Answers will vary.

Commentators in Common (page 89)

Axis Sally: chose to broadcast; was welcomed by enemy country; did not graduate from college before the war; wanted to be an actress; born in Maine

Tokyo Rose: forced to broadcast; was not welcomed by enemy country; graduated from college before the war; wanted to be a doctor; born in California

Both: nickname came from GIs; American citizen; convicted of treason; fined $10,000

Sailing Words (page 91)

1. crosstrees
2. main mast
3. foremast
4. jib
5. bow
6. stern
7. keel
8. transom
9. main boom
10. main sail
11. topmast

Character Builders (page 92)

Answers may vary. Possible answers include:

1. respect
2. perseverance
3. citizenship
4. loyalty
5. fairness
6. dedication
7. patience
8. caring
9. trust
10. responsibility

Interviewing the Captain (page 93)

Answers will vary.

Writing a Biography (page 94)

Place a circle around sentences 2, 3, 4, 5, 8, and 9.
Cross out sentences 1, 6, 7, and 10.

Words of Whitman (page 96)

1. profound
2. indecent
3. symbolic
4. devastation
5. free verse
6. firsthand
7. volume
8. assassination
9. conflict
10. editions

A Sample of Whitman's Life (page 97)

Answers will vary. Possible answers include:
1. born on Long Island
2. began writing for newspapers
3. published first edition of *Leaves of Grass*
4. published second edition of *Leaves of Grass*
5. stopped writing for newspapers
6. went to look for his brother George
7. published *Drum Taps*
8. was fired from the Department of the Interior
9. died

Whitman's Ideas (page 98)

1. Whitman understood the common people of America.
2. Family was important to Whitman.
3. Whitman loved to write.
4. Other writers respected Whitman's work.

Kinds of Poetry (page 100)

Across
2. elegy
4. poem
5. epic
7. blank verse
10. haiku
11. refrain
13. ballad
14. verse
15. rhythm

Down
1. doggerel
3. free verse
6. couplet
8. sonnet
9. rhyme
12. ode

Poetry (page 101)

Poems will vary.

Becoming a Poet (page 102)

Place a circle around sentences 4, 5, 6, and 8.
Cross out sentences 1, 2, 3, 7, 9, and 10.

Timely Vocabulary (page 104)

1. various
2. composers
3. distinctive
4. popularity
5. impressed
6. phenomenon
7. contributions
8. posthumous
9. pianists
10. syncopated
11. revival

Popular Music (page 105)

Answers will vary.

Because of Ragtime (page 106)

Answers may vary. Possible answers include:
1. People from all over heard ragtime.
2. Ragtime became popular.
3. More people had access to ragtime music.
4. Lamb went to work for a publisher.
5. Stark published their music.
6. They published Scott's music.
7. Ragtime wasn't popular anymore.
8. Joplin learned to play their piano.
9. The era of ragtime ended.
10. Ragtime was used in the movie *The Sting*.

Musical Words (page 108)

1. presto
2. allegro
3. sforzando
4. da capo
5. accelerando
6. tutti
7. fine
8. diminuendo

9. crescendo
10. adagio
11. vivace
12. con
13. molto
14. andante
15. lento

Orchestra Seating (page 109)

a. piano
b. percussion
c. timpani
d. trombones
e. tubas
f. French horns
g. clarinets
h. bassoons
i. trumpets
j. harp
k. flutes and piccolos
l. oboes
m. double basses
n. second violins
o. violas
p. first violins
q. cellos

What Did He Say? (page 110)

Answers will vary. Possible answers include:
1. morning
2. breakfast
3. wife, friend
4. dressed
5. bus, taxi
6. auditorium, orchestra hall
7. doors
8. thought
9. place, address
10. asked
11. auditorium, place
12. knocked
13. door
14. door
15. sitting
16. looked
17. evening, night
18. started, began
19. sounded
20. finished, done
21. night, evening
22. auditorium
23. wonderful, beautiful, great

24. clapped, applauded
25. very, really

Words with Feeling (page 112)

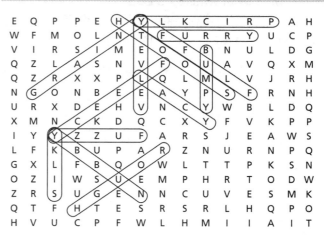

Feelings (page 113)

Answers will vary.

New Masterpieces (page 114)

1. van Gogh
2. Pollock
3. Ernst
4. van Eyck
5. Cassatt
6. van Gogh

Tricky Words (page 116)

1. allowed
2. aloud
3. dessert
4. desert
5. due
6. do
7. knew
8. new
9. know
10. no
11. past
12. passed
13. quite
14. quiet
15. than
16. then
17. Who's
18. whose
19. You're
20. your

Comparing Characters (page 117)

Answers will vary.

The Trick of Writing a Good Story (page 118)

Place a circle around sentences 1, 3, 4, 5, 6, 7, 8, 11, and 13.
Cross out sentences 2, 9, 10, 12, 14, and 15.